International Christmas

139 Easy Arrangements for Piano

by

ADA RICHTER

(with Words and Chord Symbols)

All of your favorite Carols together with many traditional Christmas Songs, Hymns and Spirituals, familiar and unfamiliar, from around the world

Theodore Presser Company

Bryn Mawr, Pennsylvania

© Copyright 1966 by Theodore Presser Co.
All Rights Reserved
Printed in U. S. A.

welcome to

International Christmas...

ERE IN THE UNITED STATES we find a wealth of tradition that has been brought together from the four corners of the earth by people of all national backgrounds, each with their own folk customs, legends and music. This is especially evident in the carols that we sing during the Christmas season.

The purpose of *International Christmas* is to present all of your favorite carols together with many traditional Christmas songs, hymns and spirituals, both familiar and unfamiliar, and identify the country with which each selection is most closely associated. Within these pages, from the opening "Everywhere, Everywhere, Christmas Tonight" to the final nostalgic "Auld Lang Syne," the Christmas message is presented in a variety of ways.

To assist you in deriving the greatest amount of pleasure from this collection, the following standards were adopted: 1) easy, full-sounding arrangements; 2) voice ranges within comfortable limits; 3) clear, easy-to-read style; 4) chord symbols to aid the playing for accordion, guitar, ukulele, chord organ, etc.; 5) verses, as many as space permits; (6) ample source information in the headings.

It is our hope that this collection will serve as a source of enlightenment and provide many hours of enjoyment during the Christmas season.

The Publisher

Contents

UNITED STATES

Everywhere, Everywhere, Christmas Tonight

Phillips Brooks
(1835-1893)

Lewis H. Redner
(1831-1908)

© Copyright 1966 by Theodore Presser Co.

ENGLAND

We Wish You A Merry Christmas

Anonymous

Anonymous

2. Oh, bring us some figgy pudding,
   Oh, bring us some figgy pudding,
   Oh, bring us some figgy pudding,
   Now bring some right here !
   Chorus

3. We won't go until we get some,
   We won't go until we get some,
   We won't go until we get some,
   So bring some right here !
   Chorus

414-41072

UNITED STATES

Toyland
(From "Babes In Toyland")

Glen MacDonough, 1903
(1870-1924)

Victor Herbert, 1903
(1859-1924)

414-41072

UNITED STATES

Jingle Bells

James Pierpont, 1857
(1822-1893)

James Pierpont, 1857
(1822-1893)

1. Dash-ing thro' the snow In a one-horse o-pen sleigh, As o'er the fields we go, A - laugh-ing all the way; The bells on bob - tail ring, And mak - ing spir - its bright; What fun it is to ride and sing A sleigh-ing song to - night!

414 - 41072

Jin – gle Bells! Jin – gle Bells! Jin – gle all the

way! Oh, what fun it is to ride In a

one – horse o – pen sleigh! one–horse o – pen sleigh!

2. Day or two ago
   I thought I'd take a ride,
   And soon Miss Fanny Bright
   Was seated at my side;
   The horse was lean and lank,
   Misfortune seem'd his lot,
   He got into a drifted bank
   And then we got upsot!
   Chorus

3. Now the ground is white,
   You should go it while you're young,
   So take the girls tonight
   And sing this sleighing song;
   Just get a bob-tailed nag,
   Two-forty for his speed,
   Then hitch him to an open sleigh
   And crack! you'll take the lead.
   Chorus

414- 41072

FRANCE

Chanson Joyeuse De Noël

A Joyful Christmas Song

French: Anonymous
English: Paul Bliss, 1924
(1872-1933)

François A. Gevaert
(1828-1908)

414- 41072

And they see that in Thee They have found the King of kings.

ENGLAND

Sleep, Holy Babe

Edward Caswall, 1850
(1814-1878)

John B. Dykes
(1823-1876)

1. Sleep, Ho - ly Babe! Up - on Thy moth - er's breast; Great Lord of earth, and sea, and sky, How sweet it is to_ see Thee lie In such a place of rest, In such_ a_ place of rest.

2. Sleep, Holy Babe! Thine angels watch around,
   All bending low with folded wings,
   Before th'incarnate King of kings,
   In rev'rent awe profound,
   In rev'rent awe profound.

3. Sleep, Holy Babe! while I with Mary gaze
   In joy upon that Face awhile,
   Upon Thy loving infant smile
   Which there divinely plays,
   Which there divinely plays.

414- 41072

BOHEMIA

Nesem Vam Noviny

Come, All Ye Shepherds

Czech: Anonymous
English: Anonymous

Anonymous, c.1750

Allegretto

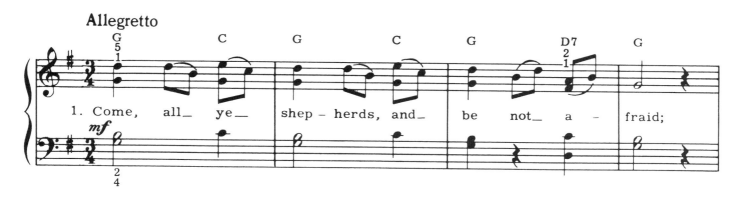

1. Come, all__ ye__ shep – herds, and__ be not__ a – fraid;

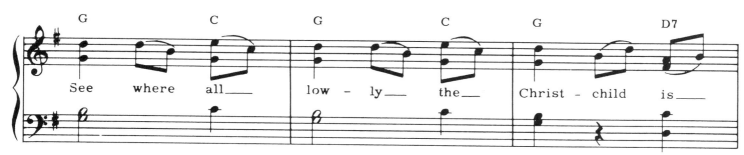

See where all___ low – ly___ the__ Christ – child is___

laid. Al – tho' in meek – ness Comes He, and meek – ness,

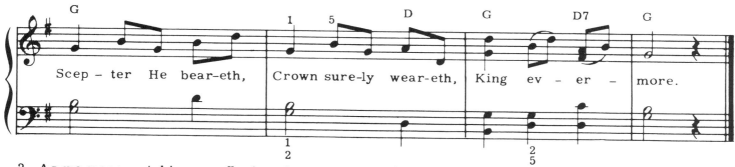

Scep – ter He bear-eth, Crown sure-ly wear-eth, King ev – er – more.

2. As we were watching our flocks where they lay,
   Shone a great brightness as clear as the day.
   Celestial singing
   On high was ringing,
   Through heav'n's blue portals
   "Good-will to mortals,
   Glory to God!"

3. Come, let us seek Him in Bethlehem's stall,
   Lord of the angels and Lord of us all.
   Kings bow before Him,
   Shepherds adore Him,
   Proclaim'd of sages
   Thro' all the ages,
   Lord evermore.

414- 41072

ENGLAND

The Twelve Days Of Christmas

Anonymous

Anonymous

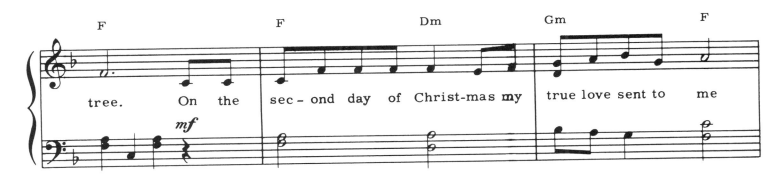

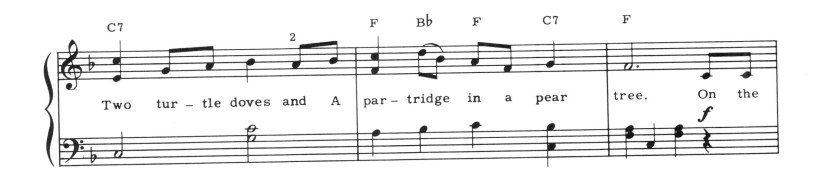

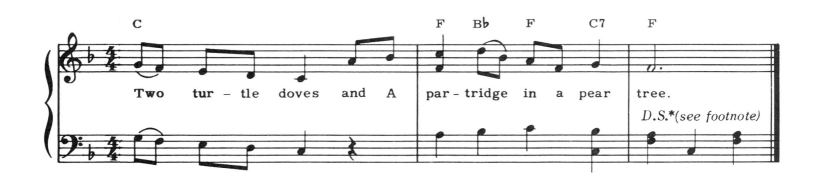

*Continue ad libitum, as follows:

On the seventh day . . . . Seven swans a-swimming, *(Measure 33 two times)*
On the eighth day . . . . Eight maids a-milking, *(Measure 33 three times)*
On the ninth day . . . . Nine ladies dancing, *(Measure 33 four times)*
On the tenth day . . . . Ten lords a-leaping, *(Measure 33 five times)*
On the eleventh day . . . . Eleven pipers piping, *(Measure 33 six times)*
On the twelfth day . . . . Twelve drummers drumming, *(Measure 33 seven times)*

414- 41072

AUSTRIA

Die Hirten Auf Dem Felde
As Lately We Watched

Austrian: Anonymous
English: Anonymous

Anonymous

3. His throne is a manger, His court is a loft,
   But troops of bright angels, in lays sweet and soft,
   Him they proclaim, our Christ by name,
   And earth, sky and air straight are fill'd with His fame.

4. Then shepherds, be joyful, salute your new King,
   Let hills and dales ring to the song that ye sing,
   Blest be the hour, welcome dem morn,
   For Christ our dear Saviour on earth now is born.

414-41072

ENGLAND

Rejoice And Be Merry

Anonymous

Anonymous

3. Likewise a bright star in the sky did appear,
   Which led the wise men from the East to draw near;
   They found the Messiah, sweet Jesus our King,
   Who brought us salvation: His praises we'll sing!

4. And when they were come, they their treasures unfold,
   And unto Him offered myrrh, incense and gold;
   So blessed forever be Jesus our King,
   Who brought us salvation: His praises we'll sing!

414-41072

AUSTRIA

Ave Maria

Ave Maria

Latin: Anonymous
English: Sir Walter Scott
(1771-1832)

Franz Schubert, 1825
(1797-1828)

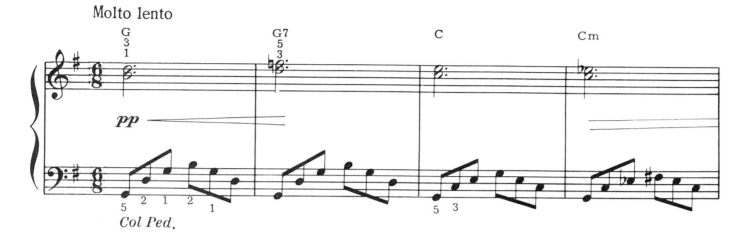

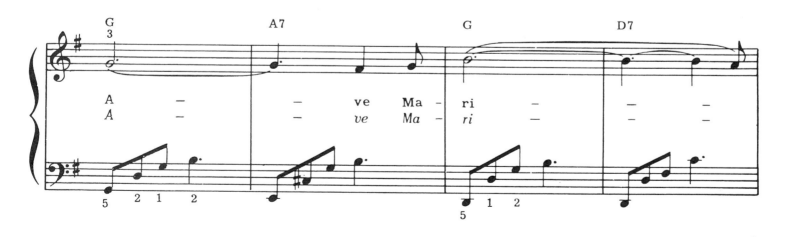

414-41072

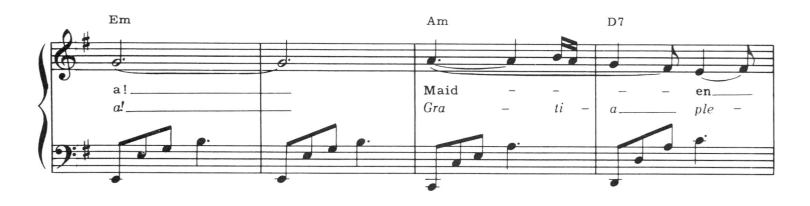

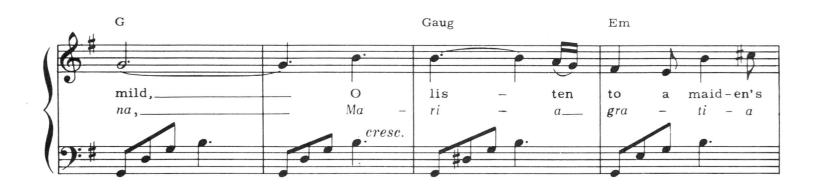

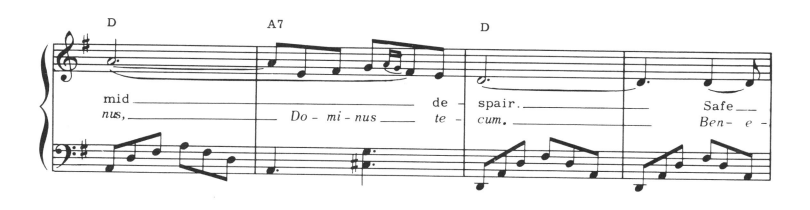

mid _____ de - spair. _____ Safe ___
nus, _____ Do - mi - nus _____ te - cum. _____ Ben - e -

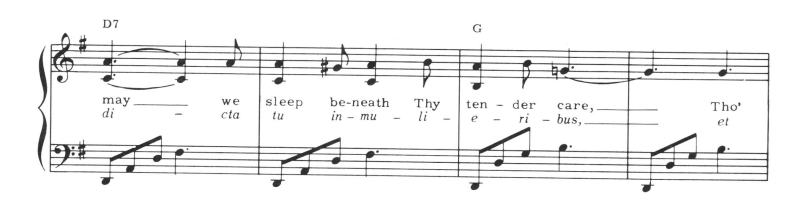

may _____ we sleep be-neath Thy ten - der care, _____ Tho'
di - cta tu in - mu - li - e - ri - bus, _____ et

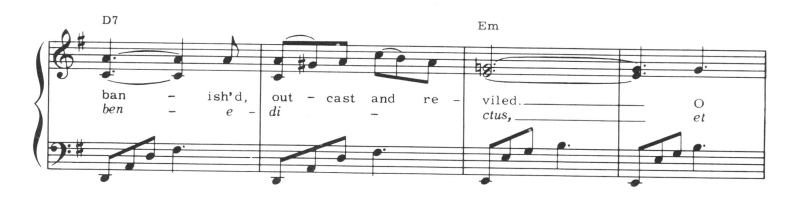

ban - ish'd, out - cast and re - viled. _____ O
ben - e - di - ctus, _____ et

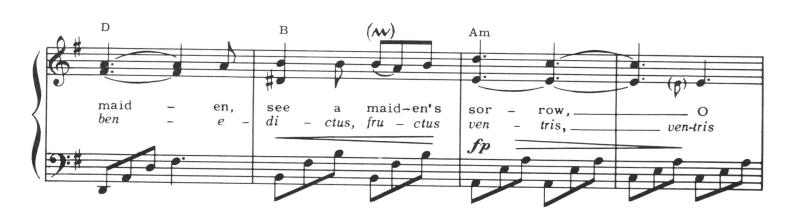

maid - en, see a maid-en's sor - row, _____ O
ben - e - di - ctus, fru - ctus ven - tris, _____ ven-tris

DENMARK

Barn Jesus I En Krybbe Laa

Child Jesus Came To Earth This Day

Danish: Hans Christian Andersen, 1849
(1805-1875)

English: Anonymous

Niels W. Gade, 1880
(1817-1890)

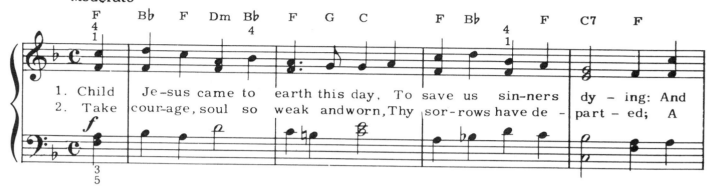

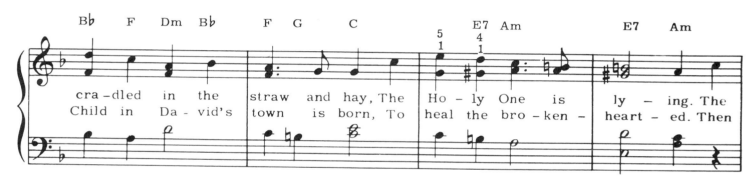

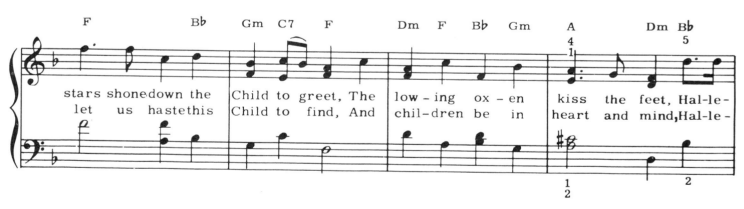

414- 41072

© Copyright 1966 by Theodore Presser Co.

ENGLAND

Ring Out, Wild Bells

Alfred Tennyson, 1849
(1809-1892)

Wolfgang A. Mozart
(1756-1791)

1. Ring out, wild bells, to the wild sky, The fly-ing cloud, the frost-y light: The year is dy-ing in the night; Ring out, wild bells, and let him die.

2. Ring out the old, ring in the new,
   Ring, happy bells, across the snow:
   The year is going, let him go;
   Ring out the false, ring in the true.

3. Ring in the valiant man and free,
   The larger heart, the kindlier hand;
   Ring out the darkness of the land,
   Ring in the Christ that is to be.

414-41072

LATIN

Adeste Fideles

O Come, All Ye Faithful

Latin: Anonymous, 18th Century
English: Frederick Oakeley, 1852
(1802-1880)

Attributed to John F. Wade, c.1740
(1711-1786)

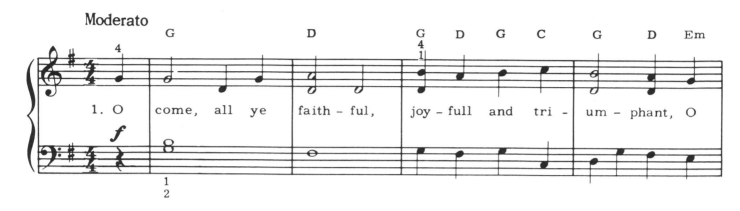

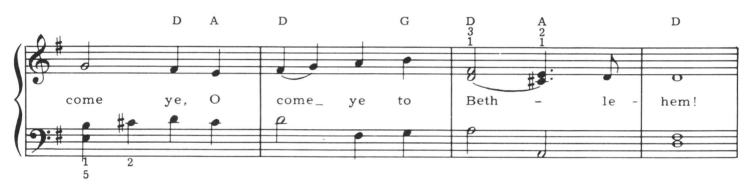

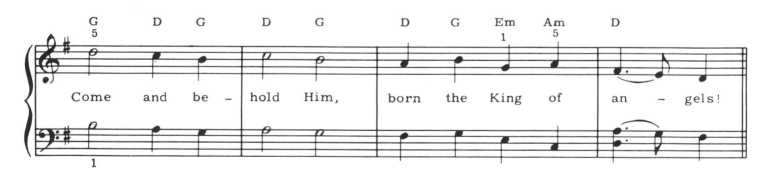

414- 41072

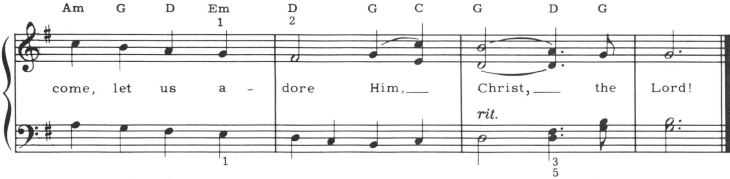

come, let us a - dore Him,___ Christ,___ the Lord!

2. Sing, choirs of angels, sing in exultation,
O sing, all ye citizens of heav'n above!
Glory to God, all glory in the highest!
Chorus

3. Yea, Lord, we greet Thee, born this happy morning,
Jesus, to Thee be all glory giv'n;
Word of the Father, now in flesh appearing!
Chorus

ENGLAND

Hark! The Glad Sound

Philip Doddridge, 1735
(1702-1751)

Thomas Haweis, 1792
(c.1733-1820)

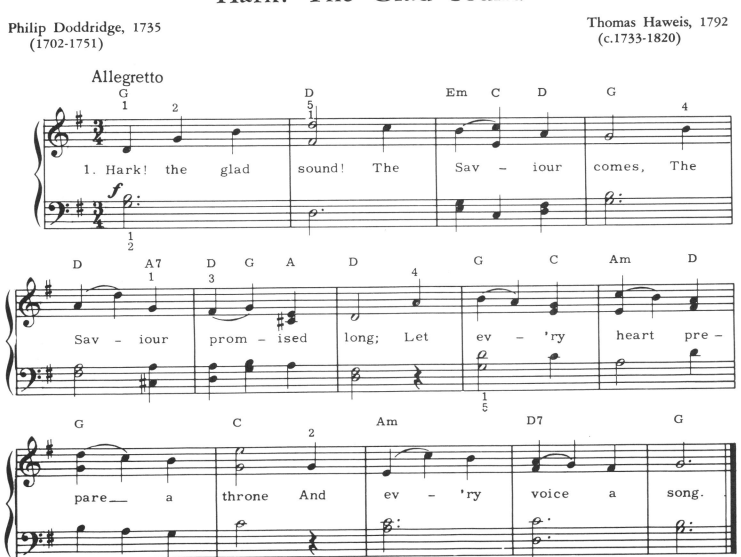

1. Hark! the glad sound! The Sav - iour comes, The
Sav - iour prom - ised long; Let ev - 'ry heart pre -
pare___ a throne And ev - 'ry voice a song.

2. He comes the broken heart to bind,
The bleeding soul to cure;
And with the treasures of His grace
T'en-rich the humble poor.

3. Our glad hosannas, Prince of Peace,
Thy welcome shall proclaim;
And heaven's eternal arches ring
With Thy beloved name.

FRANCE

Guillô, Pran Ton Tamborin

Willie, Take Your Little Drum
(Pat-A-Pan)

French: Bernard de la Monnoye, 1700
(1641-1728)

English: George W. Anthony, 1966

Bernard de la Monnoye, 1700
(1641-1728)

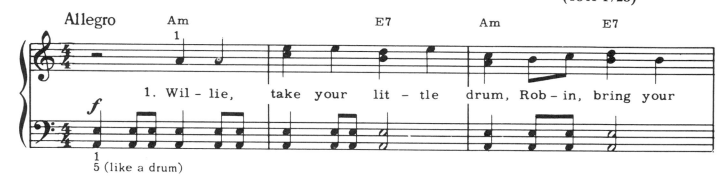

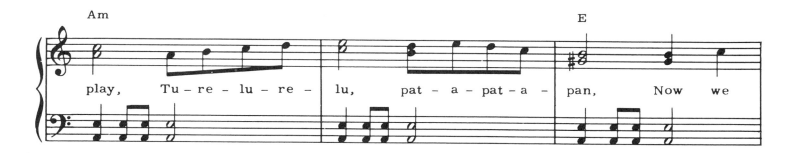

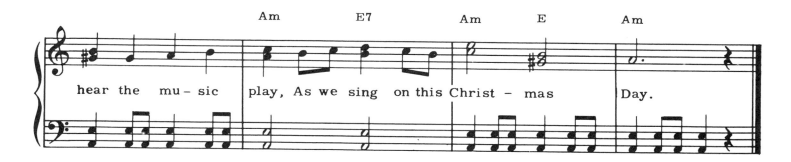

2. Shepherds in the olden days
   To the little Child gave praise.
   When they heard the music play,
   Tu-re-lu-re-lu, pat-a-pat-a-pan,
   When they heard the music play,
   They would sing on that Christmas Day.

3. Come all men and let us sing
   Our praises to the King.
   Let us hear the music play,
   Tu-re-lu-re-lu, pat-a-pat-a-pan,
   Let us hear the music play,
   For a gay, merry Christmas Day.

414-41072

UNITED STATES

Jolly Old Saint Nicholas

Anonymous

Anonymous

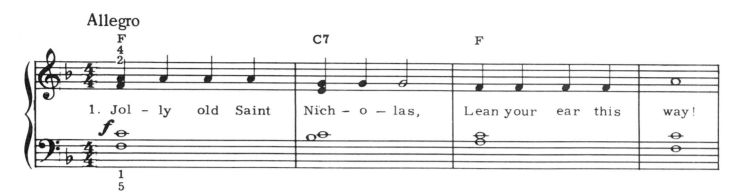

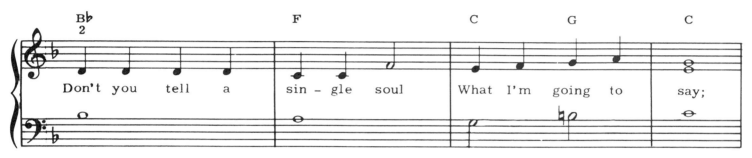

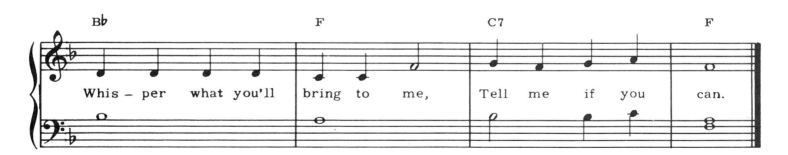

2. When the clock is striking twelve,
   When I'm fast asleep,
   Down the chimney broad and black,
   With your pack you'll creep;
   All the stockings you will find
   Hanging in a row;
   Mine will be the shortest one,
   You'll be sure to know.

3. Johnny wants a pair of skates,
   Susy wants a sled;
   Nellie wants a picture book,
   Yellow, blue and red;
   Now I think I'll leave to you
   What to give the rest;
   Choose for me, dear Santa Claus,
   You will know the best.

414- 41072

FRANCE

Cantique De Noël

O Holy Night

French: Cappeau de Roquemaure
English: John S. Dwight
(1813-1893)

Adolphe Adam, 1847
(1803-1856)

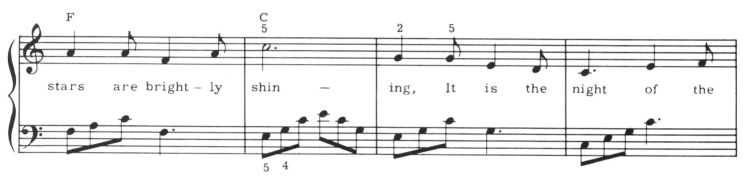

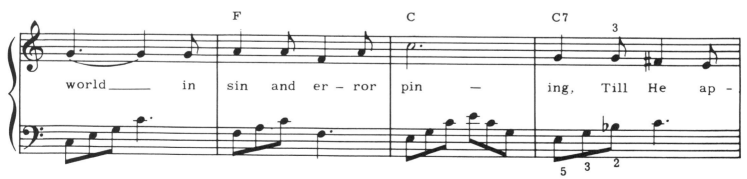

414-41072

ENGLAND

The Moon Shines Bright

Anonymous
Altered by George W. Anthony, 1966

Anonymous

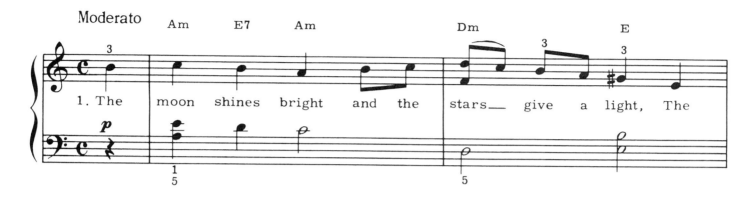

2. Awake, awake, good people all,
   Awake, and you shall hear,
   That our Lord and Saviour came to earth
   To bring you happiness and cheer.

3. The fields were green as green could be,
   When from His glorious seat
   Our blessed Father gave to us
   Little Jesus, so gentle and sweet.

4. And for the saving of our souls
   Christ died upon the cross;
   We ne'er shall do for Jesus Christ
   As He hath done for us.

5. The song is o'er, but the story lives on,
   Rekindled every year;
   God bless you all both great and small,
   And send you a joyful New year.

414-41072

Als Ich Bei Meinen Schafen Wacht

While By My Sheep
(Echo Carol)

German: Anonymous
English: Anonymous

Anonymous

2. There shall be born, so he did say,
   In Bethlehem a Child today.
   Chorus

3. There shall the Child lie in a stall,
   This Child who shall redeem us all.
   Chorus

4. This gift of God I'll cherish well,
   That ever joy my heart shall fill.
   Chorus

414-41072

ENGLAND

The Boar's Head In Hand Bear I
(The Boar's Head Carol)

Anonymous, 17th Century

Anonymous, 18th Century

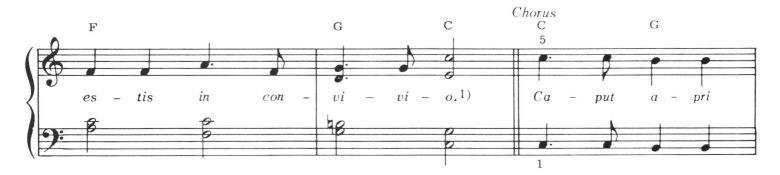

2. The boar's head I understand
   Is the rarest dish in all this land,
   Which thus bedecked with a garland gay,
   Let us *servire cantico.* 3)
   Chorus

3. Our steward hath provided this
   In honor of the King of bliss,
   Which on this day to be served is,
   In *Reginensi atrio.* 4)
   Chorus

1) Everyone who is at this feast.
2) The boar's head I bring, Giving praises to the Lord.

3) Let us serve with a song.
4) In the royal hall.

414-41072

UNITED STATES

There's A Song In The Air

Josiah G. Holland, 1872
(1819-1881)

Karl P. Harrington, 1904
(1861-1953)

2. There's a tumult of joy
   O'er the wonderful birth
   For the Virgin's sweet boy
   Is the Lord of the earth.
   Ay! the star rains its fire
       while the beautiful sing,
   For the manger of Bethlehem
       cradles the King!

3. We rejoice in the light,
   And we echo the song
   That comes down through the night
   From the heavenly throng.
   Ay! we shout to the lovely
       evangel they bring,
   And we greet in His cradle
       our Saviour and King!

414- 41072

UNITED STATES
O Little Town Of Bethlehem

Phillips Brooks, 1868
(1835-1893)

Lewis H. Redner, 1874
(1831-1908)

3. How silently, how silently
   The wondrous gift is given!
   So God imparts to human hearts
   The blessings of His heaven.
   No ear may hear His coming,
   But in the world of sin,
   Where meek souls will receive Him still,
   The dear Christ enters in.

4. O holy Child of Bethlehem!
   Descend to us, we pray;
   Cast out our sin, and enter in,
   Be born in us today.
   We hear the Christmas angels
   The great glad tidings tell;
   O come to us, abide with us,
   Our Lord Immanuel!

414-41072

Dors, Ma Colombe

Sleep, Little Dove

French: Emile Blémont
English: Charles F. Manney, 1922
    (1872-1951)

Anonymous

1. "Sleep, lit – tle Dove of mine, Sleep while the stars____ shine,"
2. "Sleep, fair – est Flow – er, Heav'n's high – est Dow – er,

Thus to her Babe____ the Vir – gin sings.
Hope of my heart,____ now close Thine eyes.

"I will watch o'er____ Thee; May dreams re – store____ Thee
Rose of the morn – ing, Pearl, all – a – dorn – ing,

Vis – ions of heav'n____ on ser – aph wings."
Sleep and dream sweet – ly of Pa – ra – dise."

414-41072

Sing, choirs of an-gels, And lull____ to____ rest The
Christ — child sleep-ing On Ma — ry's breast.

GERMANY

Alle Jahre Wieder

As Each Happy Christmas

German: Johann W. Hey
(1789-1854)
English: G. F. Kayser, 1855

Johann C. Rinck, 1837
(1770-1846)

1. As each hap-py Christ-mas Dawns on earth a — gain,

Comes the ho — ly Christ-child To the hearts of men.

2. Enters with His blessing
   Into ev'ry home,
   Guides and guards our footsteps,
   As we go and come.

3. All unknown, beside me
   He will ever stand,
   And will safely lead me,
   With His own right hand.

414-41072

FRANCE

Il Est Né, Le Divin Enfant

Christ Is Born The Holy Child

French: Anonymous
English: Marion Vree, 1959

Anonymous, 18th Century

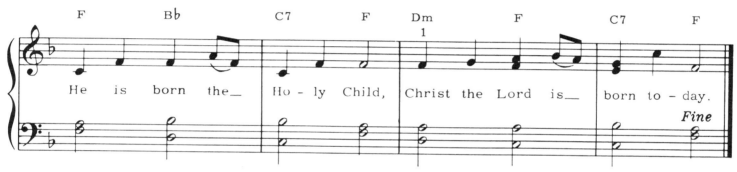

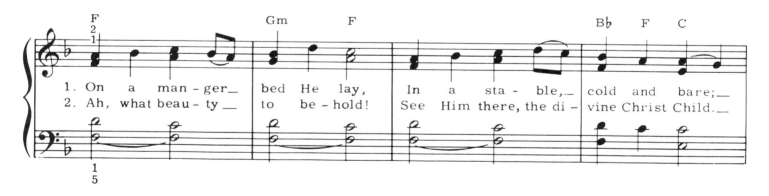

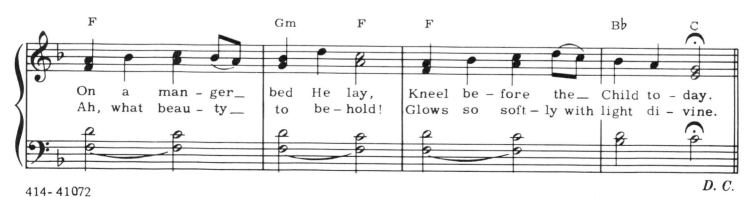

414-41072

D. C.

GERMANY

O Du Fröhliche

O Thou Joyful Day

German: Anonymous
English: Anonymous

Latin Tune: Anonymous

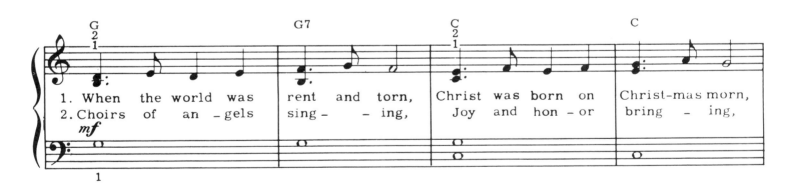

414-41072

UNITED STATES

Rise Up, Shepherd, An' Foller

Anonymous

Anonymous

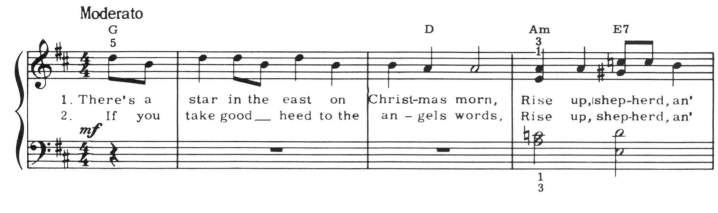

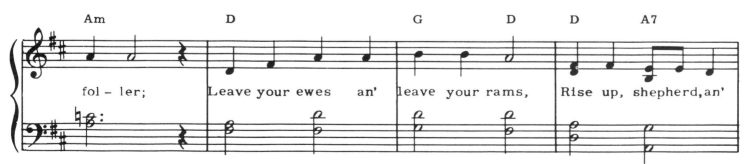

414- 41072

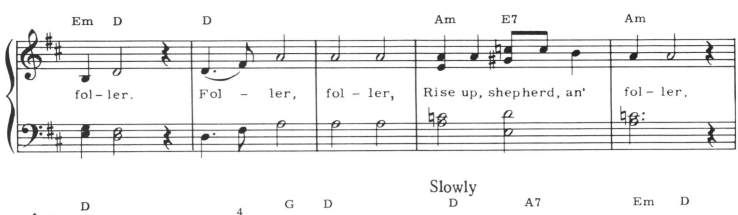

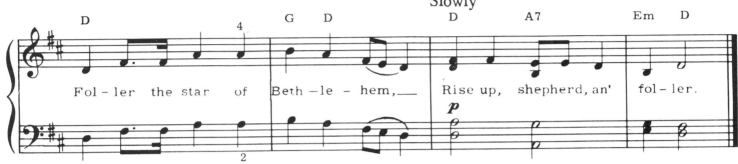

ENGLAND

Lullaby To The Christ Child

Adapted by George W. Anthony, 1966

Armenian Tune: Anonymous

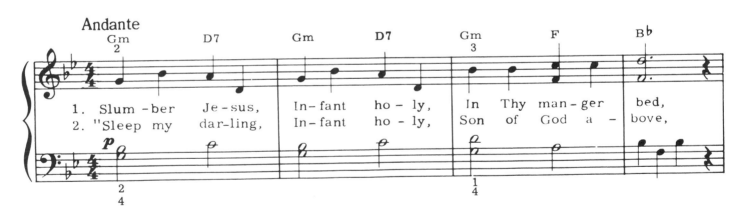

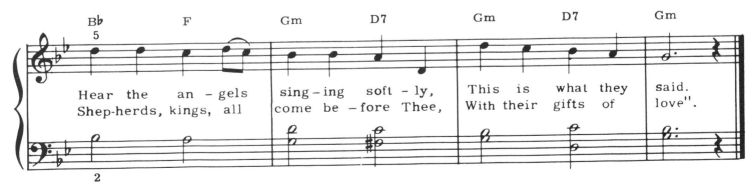

414- 41072

ENGLAND

Once In Royal David's City

Cecil F. Alexander, 1848
(1823-1895)

Henry J. Gauntlett, 1849
(1805-1876)

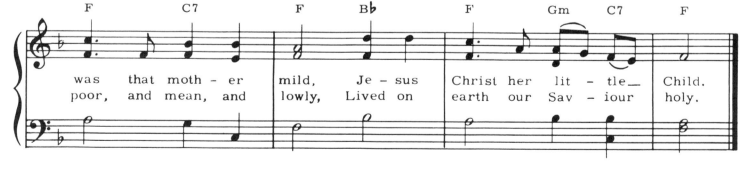

3. Jesus is our childhood's pattern,
   Day by day like us He grew;
   He was little, weak and helpless,
   Tears and smiles like us He knew:
   And He feeleth for our sadness,
   And He shareth in our gladness.

4. And our eyes at last shall see Him,
   Through His own redeeming love;
   For that Child so dear and gentle
   Is our Lord in heav'n above:
   And He leads His children on
   To the place where He has gone.

414-41072

ENGLAND

Hail! To The Lord's Anointed

James Montgomery, 1821
(1771-1854)

German Tune: Anonymous, 1784

1. Hail, to the Lord's A - noint - ed, Great
2. He comes with suc - cor speed - y To

Da-vid's great-er Son! Hail,
those who suf-fer wrong; To

in the time ap - point - ed, His
help the poor and need - y, And

reign on earth be - gun! He
bid the weak be strong; To

comes to break op - pres - sion, To
give them songs for sigh - ing, Their

set the cap - tive free; To
dark-ness turn to light, Whose

take a - way trans - gres - sion, And
souls, con - demned and dy - ing, Are

rule in eq - ui - ty.
pre - cious in His sight.

3. He shall come down like showers
Upon the fruitful earth,
Love, joy, and hope, like flowers,
Spring in His path to birth:
Before Him, on the mountains,
Shall peace, the herald, go,
And righteousness, in fountains,
From hill to valley flow.

4. To Him shall prayer unceasing
And daily vows ascend;
His kingdom still increasing,
A kingdom without end:
The tide of time shall néver
His covenant remove;
His Name shall stand forever;
That Name to us is Love.

414- 41072

Au Saint Nau

Sing Noel

French: Anonymous
English: Charles F. Manney, 1912
(1872-1951)

Anonymous

414-41072

2. In the middle of the night, Noel,
   Shone the sun as clear as day,
   And appeared an angel bright, Noel,
   Who did point us to the way.
   Chorus

3. Hastened we on nimble feet, Noel,
   And we never stopp'd to rest
   Till we saw the Virgin sweet, Noel,
   And the Holy Child on her breast.
   Chorus

LATIN

Puer Natus In Bethlehem

A Babe Is Born In Bethlehem

Latin: Anonymous, 14th Century
English: Philip Schaff, 1869

Ludvig M. Lindeman, 1869
(1812-1887)

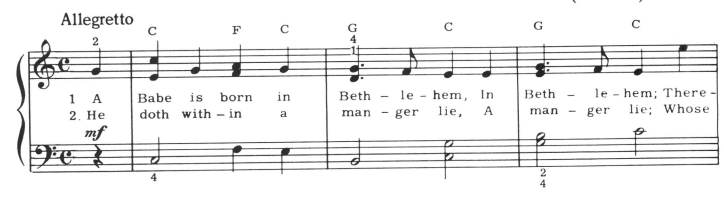

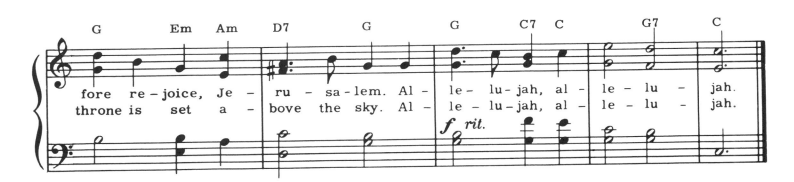

3. The wise men came, led by the star,
   Led by the star;
   Gold, myrrh and incense, brought from far.
   Allelujah, allelujah.

4. On this most blessed Jubilee,
   Blest Jubilee;
   All glory be, O God, to Thee.
   Allelujah, allelujah.

414 - 41072

ENGLAND

This Endris Nyght

The Other Night

Anonymous, 15th Century
Altered by George W. Anthony, 1966

Anonymous, 15th Century

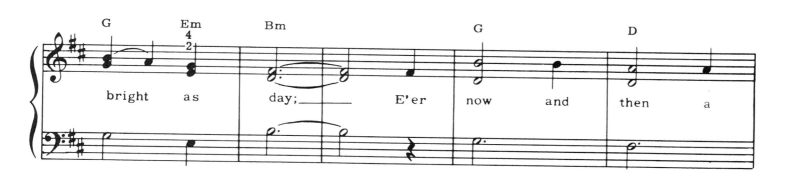

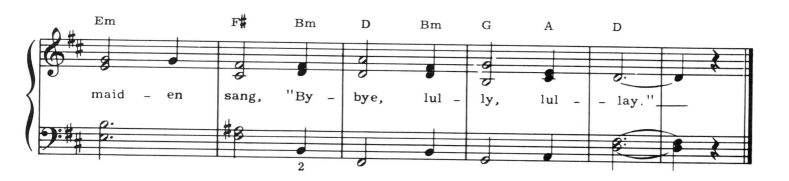

2. This lovely maiden sat and sang,
   And to her Child did say:
   "My Son, my Brother, Father dear,
   By-bye, lully, lullay."

3. "My sweetest One, my own dear Son,
   Art Thou not God alway?
   But ne'ertheless I will not cease
   To sing by-bye, lullay."

4. "Methinks it right, the King of kings
   Should lie in rich array;
   And listen to this little song
   By-bye, lully, lullay."

5. "For all Thy will I would fulfill,
   Thou knowest how I pray;
   I'll sing this song on Christmas Eve,
   By-bye, lully, lullay."

414-41072

ENGLAND

Christians, Carol Sweetly

William C. Dix
(1837-1898)

German Tune: Anonymous

1. Christians, carol sweetly, up to-day and sing!
   'Tis the happiest birthday of our holy King;
   Haste we, then, to greet Him, humble falling down,
   While our hands entwine Him, dearest Babe, a crown.

2. Crowds of snow-white angels throng the golden stair,
   All things are delightful, all things passing fair;
   Bells, clear music making, peal the news to earth,
   Chimes within make answer, all is glee and mirth.

3. Angels, Mary, Joseph, yes, I greet you all!
   Falling down in worship at the manger stall;
   For you hail our Monarch, born a child to-day
   So, with you I worship, and my homage pay.

414-41072

ENGLAND

On Christmas Night

Anonymous

Anonymous

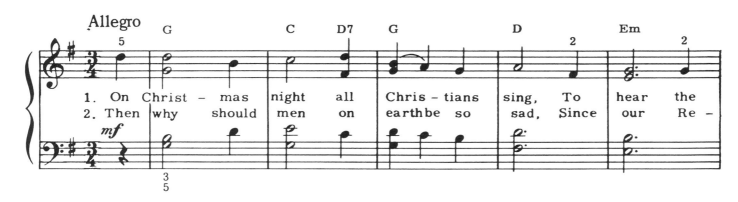

1. On Christ - mas night all Chris - tians sing, To hear the
2. Then why should men on earth be so sad, Since our Re -

news_ the an - gels bring; On Christ - mas night all
deem - er made us glad? Then why should men on

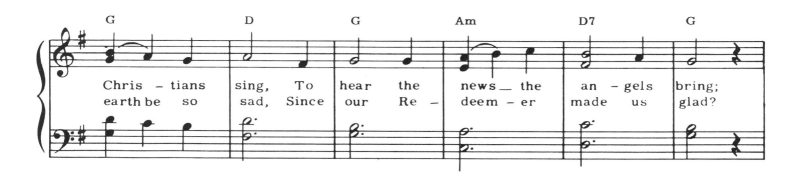

Chris - tians sing, To hear the news_ the an - gels bring;
earth be so sad, Since our Re - deem - er made us glad?

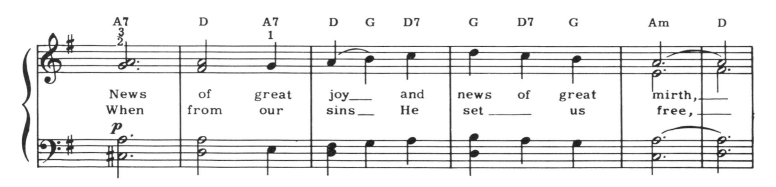

News of great joy___ and news of great mirth,
When from our sins___ He set ___ us free,

414-41072

News | of | our | mer – ci – ful | King's___ | birth.___
All | for | to | gain___ our | lib – er – ty.___

3. All out of darkness we have light,
   Which made the angels sing this night;
   All out of darkness we have light,
   Which made the angels sing this night;
   "Glory to God and peace to men,
   Now and forevermore, Amen.

UNITED STATES

Winds Through The Olive Trees

Anonymous   Anonymous

1. Winds through the ol – ive trees Soft – ly did blow,
2. Sheep on the hill – side lay White as the snow,

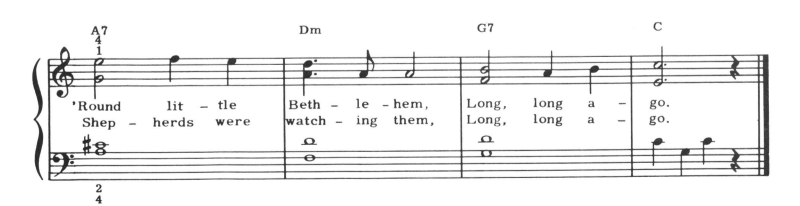

'Round lit – tle Beth – le – hem, Long, long a – go.
Shep – herds were watch – ing them, Long, long a – go.

3. Then from the starry skies
   Angels bent low,
   Singing their songs of joy,
   Long, long ago.

4. For in a manger bed,
   Cradled, we know,
   Christ came to Bethlehem,
   Long, long ago.

414- 41072

© Copyright 1966 by Theodore Presser Co.

GERMANY

Ihr Kinderlein, Kommet

O Come, Little Children

German: Christoph von Schmid, 1840
(1768-1854)
English: George W. Anthony, 1966

Johann A. P. Schulz
(1747-1800)

1. O come, little children, O come, one and all,
O come to the manger, so lowly and small;
And see what the Father has sent us tonight,
'Tis little Lord Jesus, a glorious sight.

2. He lies in a cradle, asleep on the hay,
A star shines above bright-ly showing the way;
In swaddling clothes lies the Child sweet and mild,
With angels above watching o'er the Christ-Child.

3. See Mary and Joseph with love in their eyes,
As they keep a vigil beside where He lies;
The shepherds are kneeling to worship their King,
The voices of angels in chorus all sing.

4. O come join the shepherds and worship the King,
Come see baby Jesus, the peace that He brings;
O come, little children, with glad voices raise,
And sing with the angels in heavenly praise.

414- 41072

ENGLAND

Masters In This Hall

William Morris, c.1860
(1834-1896)

French Tune: Anonymous

Moderato

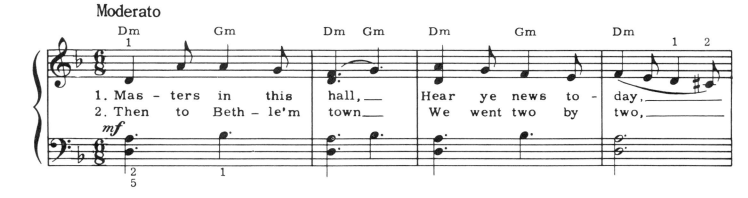

1. Mas – ters in this hall,__ Hear ye news to – day,__
2. Then to Beth – le'm town__ We went two by two,__

Brought from o – ver – seas And ev – er you I pray:
In a sor – ry place__ Heard the ox – en low:

Chorus

No – well! No – well! No – well! No – well sing we clear! Holp – en
No – well! No – well! No – well! No – well sing we loud! God to –

are all folk on earth, Born is God's Son so dear.
day hath poor folk raised And   cast a-down the proud.

3. Ox and ass Him know,
   Kneeling on their knee,
   Wondrous joy had I
   This little Babe to see:
   Chorus

4. This is Christ, the Lord
   Masters be ye glad!
   Christmas is come in,
   And no folk should be sad!
   Chorus

414- 41072

ENGLAND
A Virgin Unspotted

Anonymous

Anonymous, 1833

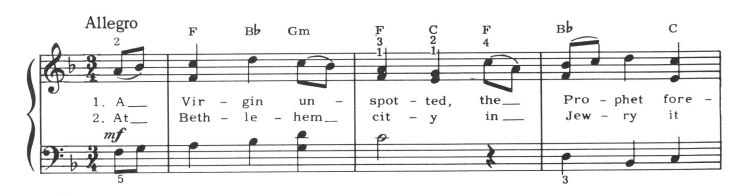

1. A— Virgin un— spot— ted, the— Pro— phet fore—
2. At— Beth— le— hem— cit— y in— Jew— ry it

told, Should bring forth a— Sav— iour, which now we be—
was That— Jo— seph and Ma— ry which to— geth— er did

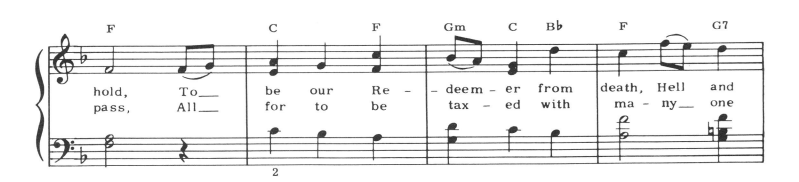

hold, To— be our Re— —deem— er from death, Hell and
pass, All— for to be tax— ed with ma— ny— one

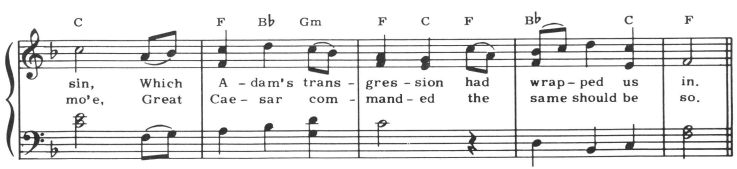

sin, Which A— dam's trans— gres— sion had wrap— ped us in.
mo'e, Which Great Cae— sar com— mand— ed the same should be so.

414- 41072

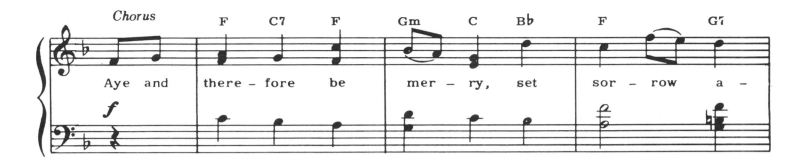

3. But when they had entered the city so fair,
   A number of people so mighty was there,
   That Joseph and Mary, whose substance was small,
   Could find in the inn there no lodging at all.
   Chorus

4. Then were they constrained in a stable to lie,
   Where horses and asses they used for to tie:
   Their lodging so simple they took it no scorn,
   But against the next morning our Saviour was born.
   Chorus

5. The King of all kings to this world being brought,
   Small store of fine linen to wrap Him was sought;
   But when she had swaddled her young Son so sweet,
   Within an ox manger she laid Him to sleep.
   Chorus

6. Then God sent an angel from heaven so high,
   To certain poor shepherds in fields where they lie,
   And bade them no longer in sorrow to stay,
   Because that our Saviour was born on this day.
   Chorus

7. Then presently after the shepherds did spy
   Vast numbers of angels to stand in the sky;
   They joyfully talked and sweetly did sing,
   To God be all glory, our heavenly King.
   Chorus

8. To teach us humility all this was done,
   And learn we from thence haughty pride for to shun;
   A manger His cradle who came from above,
   The great God of mercy, of peace and of love.
   Chorus

414-41072

ENGLAND

See, Amid The Winter's Snow

Edward Caswall, 1851
(1814-1878)

John Goss
(1800-1880)

2. Lo, within a manger lies
He, who built the starry skies;
He, who thron'd in height sublime,
Sits amid the Cherubim!
Chorus

3. Say, ye holy shepherds, say,
What your joyful news today;
Wherefore have ye left your sheep
On the lonely mountain steep?
Chorus

4. "As we watched at dead of night,
Lo, we saw a wondrous light;
Angels singing peace on earth,
Told us of the Saviour's birth."
Chorus

5 Sacred Infant, all divine,
What a tender love was Thine;
Thus to ccme from highest bliss
Down to such a world as this!
Chorus

414- 41072

ENGLAND

Blessed Be That Maid Marie

Anonymous

Anonymous

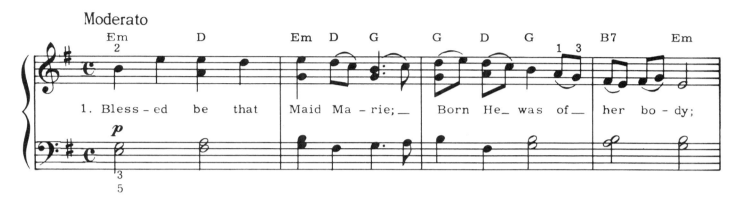

2. In a manger of an ass
   Jesu lay and lulled was;
   Born to die upon the tree
   Pro peccante homine.
   Chorus

3. Sweet and blissful was the song
   Chanted of the angel throng;
   "Peace on earth," alleluia.
   In excelsis gloria.
   Chorus

4. Fare three kings from far-off land,
   Incense, gold and myrrh in hand;
   In Bethlehem the Babe they see,
   Stelle ducti lumine.
   Chorus

5. Make we merry on this fest,
   In quo Christus natus est;
   On this Child I pray you call,
   To assoil and save us all.
   Chorus

414- 41072

ENGLAND

The Seven Joys Of Mary

Anonymous

Anonymous

Allegretto

1. The first good joy that Ma—ry had, It was the joy of one;— To

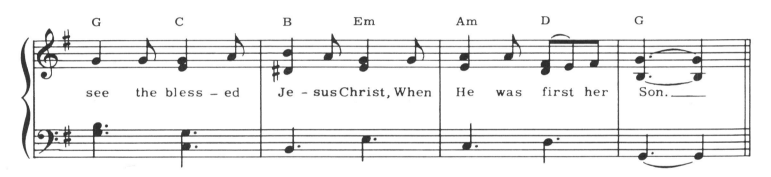

see the bless—ed Je—susChrist, When He was first her Son.—

Chorus

When He was first her Son, Good Lord; And hap—py may we be;— Praise

Fa—ther, Son, and Ho—ly Ghost, To all e—ter—ni—ty.—

414- 41072

2. The next good joy that Mary had,
It was the joy of two;
To see her own Son Jesus Christ,
Making the lame to go.
Chorus: Making the lame to go,
Good Lord; *etc.*

3. The next good joy that Mary had,
It was the joy of three;
To see her own Son Jesus Christ,
Making the blind to see.
Chorus: Making the blind to see,
Good Lord; *etc.*

4. The next good joy that Mary had,
It was the joy of four;
To see her own Son Jesus Christ,
Reading the Bible o'er.
Chorus: Reading the Bible o'er,
Good Lord; *etc.*

5. The next good joy that Mary had,
It was the joy of five;
To see her own Son Jesus Christ,
Raising the dead to life.
Chorus: Raising the dead to life,
Good Lord; *etc.*

6. The next good joy that Mary had,
It was the joy of six,
To see her own Son Jesus Christ,
Upon the Crucifix,
Chorus: Upon the Crucifix,
Good Lord; *etc.*

7. The next good joy that Mary had,
It was the joy of seven,
To see her own Son Jesus Christ,
Ascending into heav'n.
Chorus: Ascending into heav'n,
Good Lord; *etc.*

FRANCE

Le Sommeil de l'Enfant Jésus
The Sleep Of The Child Jesus

French: Anonymous
English: Charles F. Manney, 1918
(1872-1951)

Anonymous

2. Girded by lilies undefiled,
Sleep, sleep, sleep, thou little Child:
Angels robed in white,
Shining seraphs bright,
Hover there above the mighty Lord of love.

3. Greeted by shepherds from the wild,
Sleep, sleep, sleep, thou little Child:
Angels robed in white,
Shining seraphs bright,
Hover there above the mighty Lord of love.

414-41072

GERMANY

Es Ist Ein' Ros' Entsprungen

Lo, How A Rose E'er Blooming

German: Anonymous
English: Theodore Baker, 1894
     (1851-1934)

Anonymous, 1599

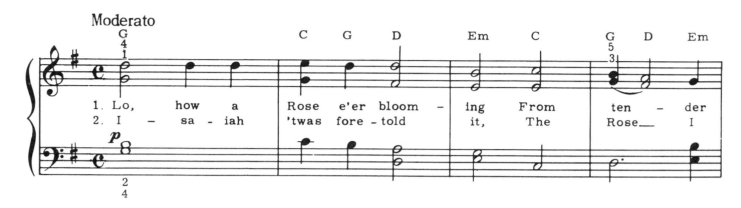

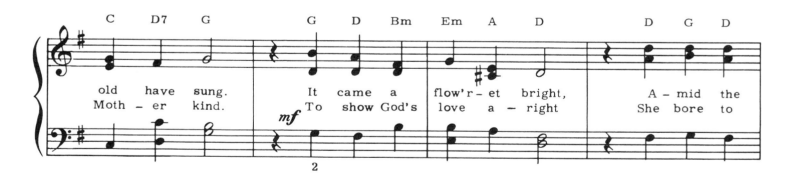

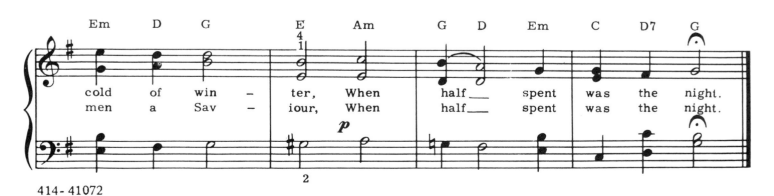

414- 41072

ENGLAND

We Saw A Light Shine Out Afar
(The Golden Carol)

Anonymous   Anonymous

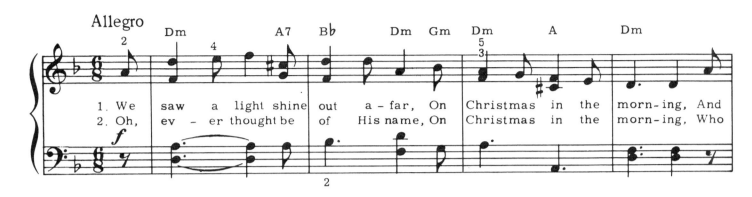

1. We saw a light shine out a-far, On Christmas in the morn-ing, And
2. Oh, ev – er thought be of His name, On Christmas in the morn-ing, Who

straight we knew it was Christ's star, Bright beam-ing in the morn – ing, Then
bore for us both grief and shame, Af – flic – tions sharp – est scorn – ing, And

did we fall on bend – ed knee, On Christ-mas in the morn – ing, And
may we die, when death shall come, On Christ-mas in the morn – ing, And

prais'd the Lord, who'd let us see His glo – ry at the dawn – ing.
see in heav'n, our glo – ri'us home, That Star of Christ-mas morn – ing.

414- 41072

ENGLAND

Hark! The Herald Angels Sing

Charles Wesley, 1739
(1707-1788)
Altered by George Whitefield, 1753
(1714-1770)

Felix Mendelssohn, 1840
(1809-1847)
Adapted by William H. Cummings, 1855
(1831-1915)

1. Hark! the her - ald an-gels sing, "Glo - ry to the new-born King;

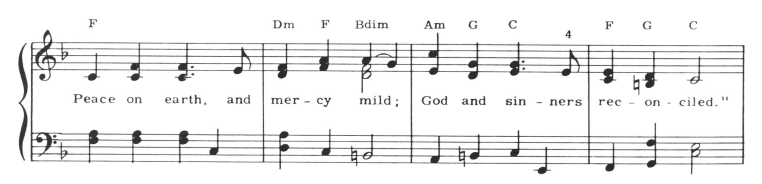

Peace on earth, and mer - cy mild; God and sin - ners rec - on - ciled."

Joy - ful, all ye na -tions, rise, Join the tri -umph of the skies;

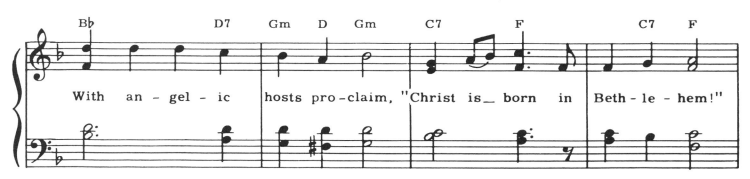

With an - gel - ic hosts pro-claim, "Christ is_ born in Beth - le - hem!"

414- 41072

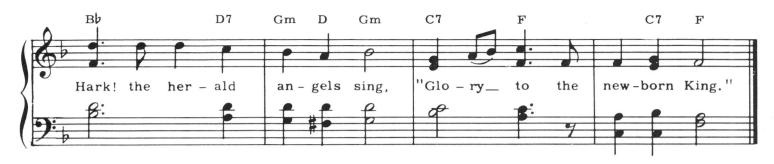

Hark! the her – ald an – gels sing, "Glo – ry__ to the new-born King."

2. Christ, by highest heaven adored,
   Christ, the everlasting Lord:
   Long desired, behold Him come,
   Finding here His humble home.
   Veiled in flesh the God-head see,
   Hail th'incarnate Deity!
   Pleased as man with men to dwell,
   Jesus our Immanuel.
   Hark! the herald angels sing,
   "Glory to the new-born King."

3. Hail the heav'n-born Prince of Peace!
   Hail the Sun of righteousness!
   Light and life to all He brings,
   Risen with healing in His wings.
   Mild He lays His glory by,
   Born that man no more may die,
   Born to raise the sons of earth,
   Born to give them second birth.
   Hark! the herald angels sing,
   "Glory to the new-born King."

UNITED STATES

I Heard The Bells On Christmas Day

Henry W. Longfellow, 1863
(1807-1882)

John Baptiste Calkin, 1872
(1827-1905)

1. I heard the bells on Christ-mas day Their old fa – mil – iar car – ols play, And
2. I thought how, as the day had come, The bel-fries of all Christ-en-dom Had

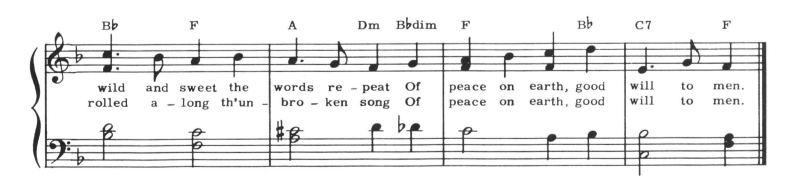

wild and sweet the words re – peat Of peace on earth, good will to men.
rolled a – long th'un – bro – ken song Of peace on earth, good will to men.

3. And in despair I bow'd my head:
   "There is no peace on earth," I said,
   "For hate is strong, and mocks the song
   Of peace on earth, good will to men."

4. Then pealed the bells more loud and deep:
   "God is not dead, nor doth he sleep;
   The wrong shall fail, the right prevail,
   With peace on earth, good will to men."

414- 41072

Gather Around The Christmas Tree

John H. Hopkins
(1820-1891)

John H. Hopkins
(1820-1891)

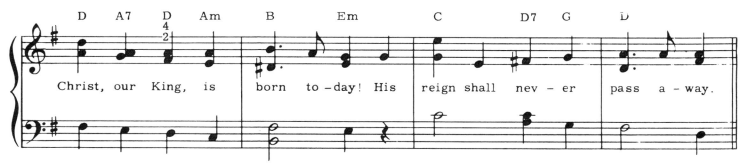

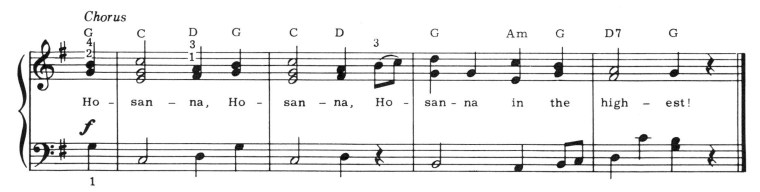

2. Gather around the Christmas tree!
   Gather around the Christmas tree!
   Once the pride of the mountain side,
   Now cut down to grace our Christmastide:
   For Christ from heav'n to earth came down,
   To gain, through death, a nobler crown.
   Chorus

3. Gather around the Christmas tree!
   Gather around the Christmas tree!
   Ev'ry bough bears a burden now;
   They are gifts of love for us, we trow:
   For Christ is born, His love to show,
   And give good gifts to men below.
   Chorus

414-41072

ENGLAND

Let Our Gladness Know No End

Anonymous

Bohemian Tune: Anonymous

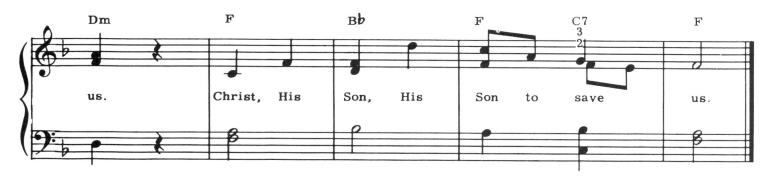

2. See the loveliest blooming rose,
   Hallelujah!
   From the branch of Jesse grows,
   Hallelujah!
   Chorus

3. Into flesh is made the word,
   Hallelujah!
   'Tis our refuge, Christ the Lord,
   Hallelujah!
   Chorus

414-41072

ENGLAND

Well-A-Day! Well-A-Day!
(Old Yorkshire Gooding Carol)

Anonymous   Anonymous

Well - a - day!__ Well - a - day! Christ-mas too__ soon goes a - way,

Then your good - ing we do pray, For the good-time will not stay.

We are not beg - gars that beg__ from door__ to door,

But neigh - bors' chil - dren you__ have known be - fore;__ So

good - ing pray, we can — not stay, We can — not stay, But must a - way,

For the Christ — mas will not stay; Well - a - day!__ Well - a - day!

ENGLAND

Glad Christmas Bells

Anonymous

Anonymous

Vivace

1. Glad Christmas bells, your mu — sic tells The sweet and pleas - ant sto - ry; How come to earth, in low - ly birth, The Lord of life and glo - ry.
2. No pal - ace hall its ceil - ing tall His king - ly head spread o - ver; There on - ly stood a__ sta - ble rude, The heav'n-ly Babe to cov - er.

3. Nor raiment gay, as there He lay,
   Adorned the Infant stranger;
   Poor, humble Child of mother mild,
   She laid Him in a manger.

4. But from afar, a splendid star
   The wisemen westward turning;
   The livelong night saw pure and bright,
   Above His birthplace burning.

414- 41072

ENGLAND

Infant So Gentle

Anonymous

French Tune: Anonymous

1. In – fant so gen – tle, so pure and so sweet,
2. In – fant so ho – ly, so meek and so mild,

Love from Thy ti – ny eyes sin – ners doth greet.
We come to wel – come Thee, our dear Christ– child.

Ten – d'rest words fail all Thy beau – ty to show,
We can – not tell Thee how much we do need,

We must a – dore Thee, if Thee we would know.
Thy pre – cious pre – sence; if all sin – ners take heed.

Brich An, Du Schönes Morgenlicht

Break Forth, O Beauteous Heavenly Light

German: Johann Rist
(1607-1667)
English: John Troutbeck
(1832-1899)

Johann Schop, 1641
Adapted by Johann S. Bach
(1685-1750)

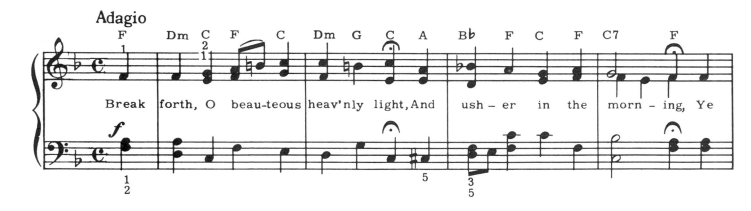

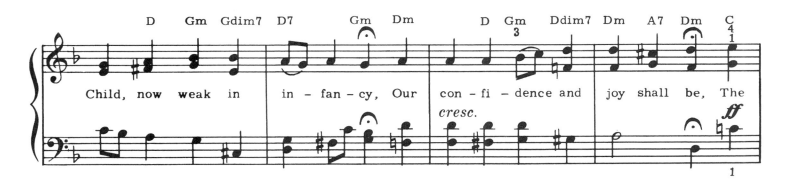

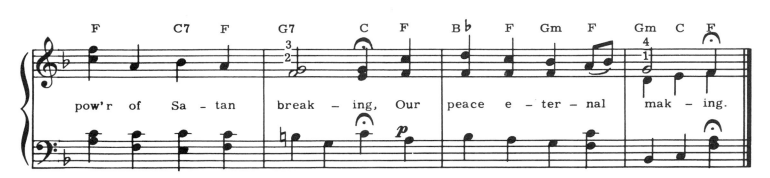

414- 41072

ENGLAND

While Shepherds Watched Their Flocks

Nahum Tate, 1708
(1652-1715)

Arr. from George F. Handel, 1728
(1685-1759)

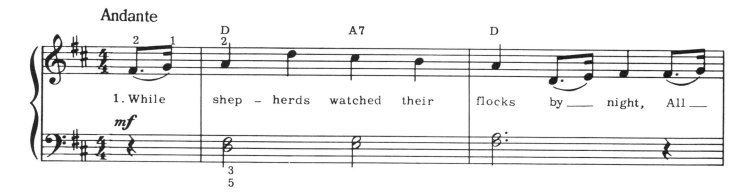

1. While shep – herds watched their flocks by ___ night, All ___

seat – ed on the ___ ground, The an – gel of the Lord came down, And

glo – ry shone a – round, And glo – ry shone a – round.

2. "Fear not!" said he for mighty dread.
   Had seized their troubled mind,
   "Glad tidings of great joy I bring,
   To you and all mankind,
   To you and all mankind."

3. "To you, in David's town this day,
   Is born of David's line,
   The Saviour, who is Christ the Lord;
   And this shall be the sign,
   And this shall be the sign."

4. "The heav'nly Babe you there shall find
   To human view displayed,
   All meanly wrapped in swathing bands,
   And in a manger laid,
   And in a manger laid."

5. "All glory be to God on high,
   And to the earth be peace:
   Good-will henceforth from heaven to men
   Begin and never cease,
   Begin and never cease!"

SCOTLAND

A Child Is Born To You Today
(Baloo, Lammy)

Anonymous

Anonymous, 17th Century

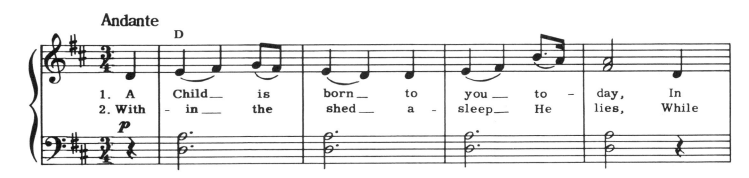

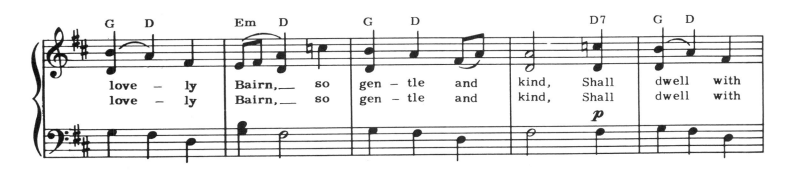

414- 41072

UNITED STATES

Up On The Housetop

Benjamin R. Hanby

Benjamin R. Hanby

Allegretto

Chorus

2. First comes the stocking of little Nell,
   Oh, dear Santa, fill it well;
   Give her a dollie that laughs and cries,
   One that will open and shut her eyes.
   Chorus

3. Next comes the stocking of little Will,
   Oh, just see what a glorious fill!
   Here is a hammer and a lots of tacks,
   Also a ball and whip that cracks.
   Chorus

414-41072

Wie Schön Leuchtet Der Morgenstern

How Brightly Beams The Morning Star

German: Philip Nicolai, 1598
and J. A. Schlegel (1721-1793)
English: Catherine Winkworth, 1863
(1829-1878)

Philip Nicolai, 1598
(1556-1608)

2. Through Thee alone can we be blest;
Then deep be on our hearts imprest
The love that Thou hast borne us;
So make us ready to fulfil
With burning zeal Thy holy will,
Though men may vex or scorn us;
Saviour, let us never lose Thee,
For we choose Thee, Thirst to know Thee;
All we are and have we owe Thee!

3. O praise to Him who came to save,
Who conquer'd death and burst the grave;
Each day new praise resoundeth
To Him the Lamb who once was slain,
The friend whom none shall trust in vain
Whose grace for ay aboundeth;
Sing, ye heavens, tell the story
Of His glory, Till His praises
Flood with light earth's darkest places!

414- 41072

ITALY

Veni, Emmanuel

O Come, O Come, Emmanuel

Latin: Anonymous, c.9th Century
English: John M. Neale, 1851
(1818-1866)

Anonymous, 13th Century
Adapted by Thomas Helmore, 1854
(1811-1890)

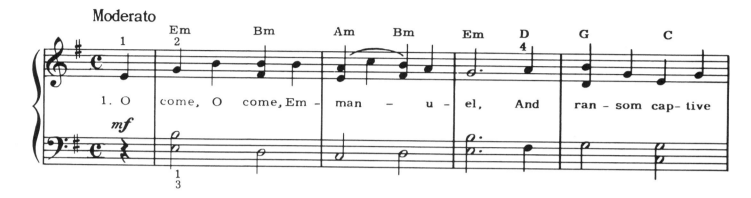

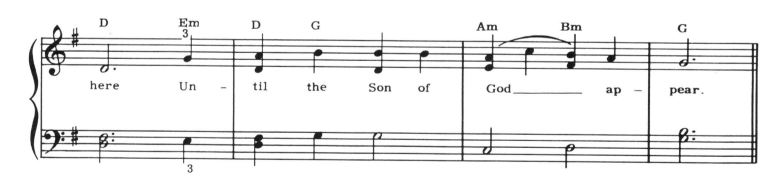

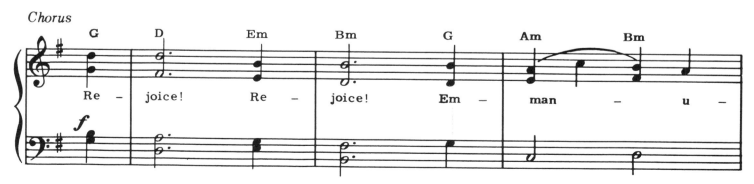

414- 41072

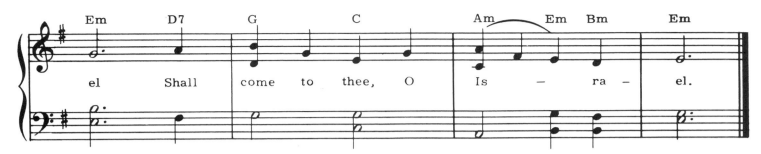

el   Shall   come to thee,   O   Is — ra — el.

2. O come, Thou Rod of Jesse, free
   Thine own from Satan's tyranny;
   From depths of hell thy people save,
   And give them vict'ry o'er the grave.
   Chorus

3. O come, Thou Day-Spring, come and cheer
   Our spirits by Thine advent here;
   Disperse the gloomy clouds of night,
   And death's dark shadows put to flight.
   Chorus

4. O come, Thou Key of David, come,
   And open wide our heav'nly home;
   Make safe the way that leads on high,
   And close the path to misery.
   Chorus

5. O come, O come, Thou Lord of might,
   Who to Thy tribes, on Sinai's height,
   In ancient times did'st give the law,
   In cloud, and majesty and awe.
   Chorus

ENGLAND

Sleep, My Saviour, Sleep

Sabine Baring-Gould
(1834-1924)

Bohemian Tune: Anonymous

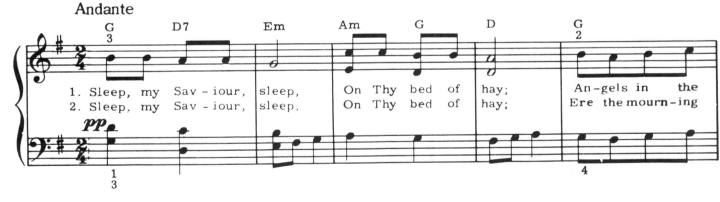

1. Sleep, my Sav-iour, sleep,   On Thy bed of hay;   An-gels in the
2. Sleep, my Sav-iour, sleep,   On Thy bed of hay;   Ere the mourn-ing

span-gled heav-en   Sing their glad-some   Christ-mas car-ols   Till the break of   day.
An — gel com-eth   To the moon-lit   ol — ive gar-den   Wip-ing tears a —   way.

3. Sleep, my Saviour, sleep
   Sweet on Mary's breast,
   Now the shepherds kneel adoring,
   Now the mother's heart is joyous,
   Take Thy happy rest.

4. Sleep, my Saviour, sleep,
   Sweet on Mary's breast,
   Crucified with wounds and bruises,
   Bleeding, purple stained, disfigured,
   One day Thou wilt rest.

414- 41072

ENGLAND

Wassail, Wassail, All Over The Town

Anonymous

Anonymous, 18th Century

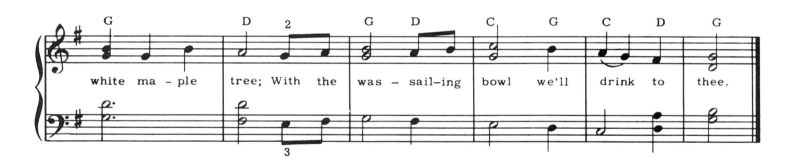

2. So here is a Cherry[1] and to his right cheek,
Pray God send our master a good piece of beef,
And a good piece of beef that may we all see;
With the wassailing bowl we'll drink to thee.

3. And here is to Dobbin[1] and to his right eye,
Pray God send our master a good Christmas pie,
And a good Christmas pie that may we all see;
With our wassailing bowl we'll drink to thee.

4. So here is to Broad May[2] and to her broad horn,
May God send our master a good crop of corn,
And a good crop of corn that may we all see;
With the wassailing bowl we'll drink to thee.

5. And here is to Fillpail[2] and to her left ear,
Pray God send our master a happy New Year,
And a happy New Year as e'er he did see;
With our wassailing bowl we'll drink to thee.

6. Come, butler, come fill us a bowl of the best,
Then we hope that your soul in heaven may rest;
But if you do draw us a bowl of the small,
Then down shall go butler, bowl and all.

7. Then here's to the maid in the lily white smock,
Who tripped to the door and slipped back the lock;
Who tripped to the door and pulled back the pin,
For to let these jolly wassailers in.

1) Name of a horse.   *2) Name of a cow.*

414- 41072

© Copyright 1966 by Theodore Presser Co.

ENGLAND

When Joseph Was An Old Man
(The Cherry-Tree Carol)

Anonymous   Anonymous

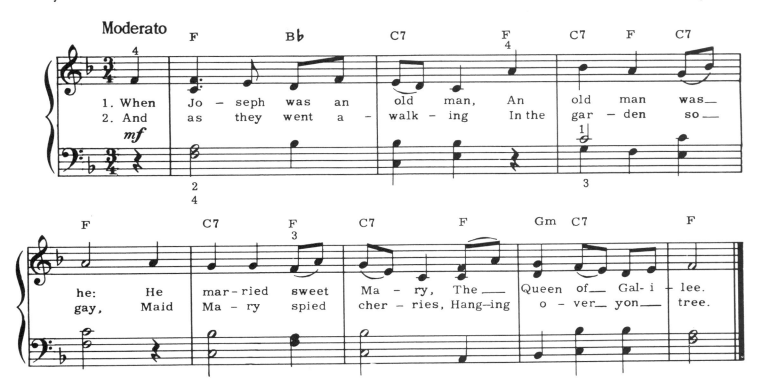

1. When Joseph was an old man, An old man was he: He married sweet Mary, The Queen of Galilee.

2. And as they went a-walking In the garden so gay, Maid Mary spied cherries, Hanging over yon tree.

3. Then Mary said to Joseph
   With her sweet lips so mild,
   "Pluck those cherries, Joseph,
   For to give to my Child."

4. And then replied Joseph
   With words so unkind,
   "I will pluck no cherries
   For to give to thy Child."

5. Said Mary to the cherry tree,
   "Bow down to my knee,
   That I may pluck cherries
   By one, two and three."

6. The uppermost sprig then
   Bowed down to her knee,
   "Thus you may see, Joseph,
   These cherries are for me."

7. "O eat your cherries, Mary,
   O eat your cherries now,
   O eat your cherries, Mary,
   That grow upon the bough."

8. As Joseph was a-walking
   He heard angels sing,
   This night there shall be born
   Our heavenly King.

9. "He neither shall be born
   In house nor in hall,
   Nor in the place of Paradise,
   But in an ox-stall.

10. "He shall not be clothed
    In purple nor pall;
    But all in fair linen,
    As wear babies all.

11. "He shall not be rocked
    In silver nor gold,
    But in a wooden cradle
    That rocks on the mould.

12. "He neither shall be christened
    In milk nor in wine,
    But in pure spring-well water
    Fresh sprung from Bethine."

13. Mary took her Baby,
    She dressed Him so sweet,
    She laid Him in a manger
    All there for to sleep.

14. As she stood over Him
    She heard angels sing,
    "Oh, bless our dear Saviour,
    Our heavenly King."

414- 41072

ENGLAND

Listen, Lordlings, Unto Me

H. R. Bramley, 1833

French Tune: Anonymous, 16th Century

414-41072

© Copyright 1966 by Theodore Presser Co.

Chorus

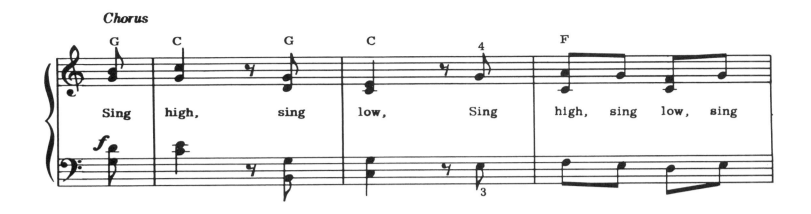

Sing high, sing low, Sing high, sing low, sing

to and fro, Go tell it out with speed, Cry

out, and shout all round a – bout That Christ is born in – deed.

2. Shepherds lay afield that night to keep the silly sheep,
Hosts of angels shining bright, came down from heaven's steep.
Tidings, tidings, unto you: to you the Christ is born,
Purer than the drops of dew and brighter than the morn.
Chorus

3. Onward, then, the angels sped, the shepherds onward went,
God was in His manger bed, in worship low they bent.
In the morning see ye mind, my masters one and all,
At the altar Him to find who lay within the stall.
Chorus

414-41072

ENGLAND

The Babe Of Bethlehem

Anonymous

Anonymous

3. For not to sit on David's throne
   With worldly pomp and joy,
   He came for sinners to atone
   And Satan to destroy.
   Chorus

4. Well may we sing a Saviour's birth,
   Who need the grace so given,
   And hail His coming down to earth,
   Who raises us to heaven.
   Chorus

414-41072

ENGLAND

What Child Is This?

William C. Dix, c.1865
(1837-1898)

Tune: Greensleeves, 16th Century

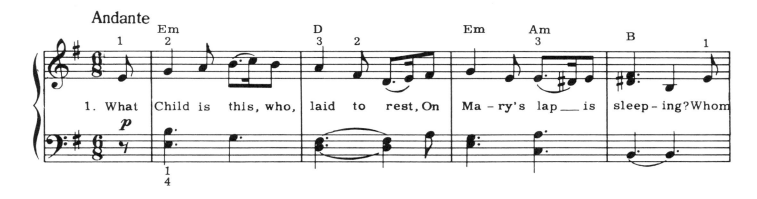

1. What Child is this, who, laid to rest, On Ma-ry's lap __ is sleep-ing? Whom

an-gels greet with an-thems sweet, While shep-herds watch __ are keep-ing?

Chorus

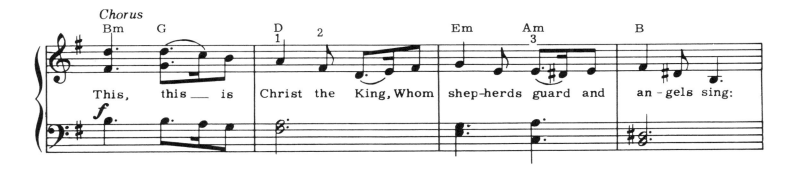

This, this __ is Christ the King, Whom shep-herds guard and an-gels sing:

Haste, haste __ to bring Him laud, The Babe, the Son of Ma-ry.

2. Why lies He in such mean estate
   Where ox and ass are feeding?
   Good Christian, fear: for sinners here
   The silent Word is pleading.
   Chorus

3. So bring Him incense, gold and myrrh,
   Come, peasant, King to own Him;
   The King of kings salvation brings,
   Let loving hearts enthrone Him.
   Chorus

414-41072

FRANCE

Marche Des Rois

March Of The Kings

French: Anonymous
English: George W. Anthony, 1966

Anonymous, 13th Century

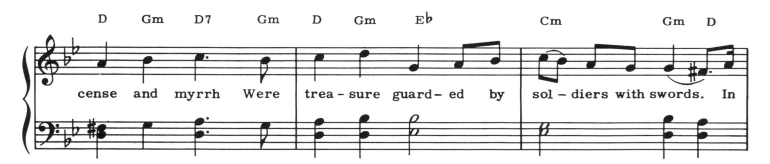

414-41072

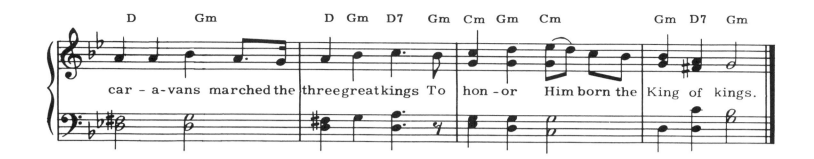

car - a - vans marched the three great kings To hon - or Him born the King of kings.

GERMANY

Vom Himmel Hoch, Da Komm' Ich Her

From Heaven Above To Earth I Come

German: Martin Luther, 1535
    (1483-1546)

English: Catherine Winkworth, 1855
    (1827-1878)

Anonymous, 1539

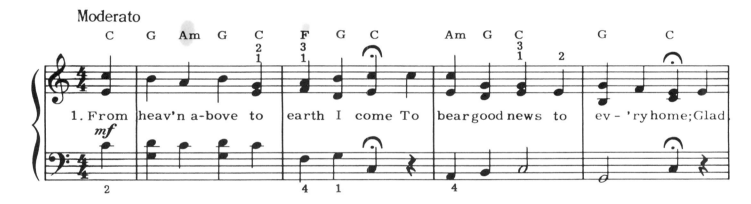

1. From heav'n a-bove to earth I come To bear good news to ev - 'ry home; Glad

tid - ings of great joy I bring. Where-of I now will say and sing.

2. To you this night is born a Child
    Of Mary, chosen virgin mild;
    This little Child, of lowly birth,
    Shall be the joy of all the earth.

3. This is the Christ, our God and Lord,
    Who in all need shall aid afford;
    He will Himself your Saviour be
    From all your sins to set you free.

4. Ah, dearest Jesus, holy Child,
    Make Thee a bed, soft, undefiled,
    Within my heart, that it may be
    A quiet chamber kept for Thee.

5. Glory to God in highest heaven,
    Who unto us His Son hath given!
    While angels sing with pious mirth
    A glad new year to all the earth.

GERMANY

Fröhlich Soll Mein Herze Springen

All My Heart This Night Rejoices

German: Paulus Gerhardt, 1656
(1607-1676)

English: Catherine Winkworth, 1858
(1827-1878)

Johann Georg Ebeling, 1666
(1637-1676)

Maestoso

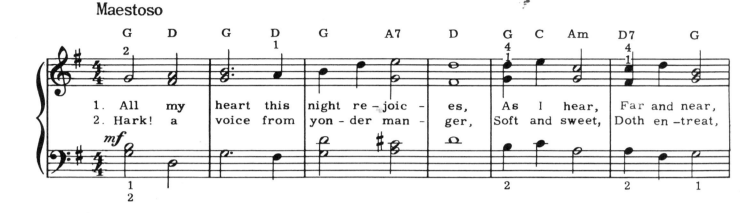

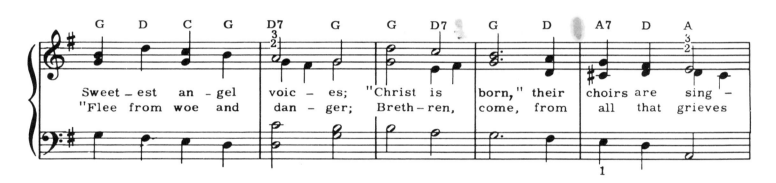

3. Come then, let us hasten yonder;
   Here let all
   Great and small
   Kneel in awe and wonder;
   Love Him who with love is yearning;
   Hail the star
   That from far
   Bright with hope is burning.

4. Blessed Saviour, let me find Thee;
   Keep Thou me
   Close to Thee,
   Cast me not behind Thee:
   Life of life, my heart Thou stillest,
   Calm I rest
   On Thy breast,
   All this void Thou fillest.

414-41072

El Desembre Congelat

As December's Frosty King
(The Three Kings)

Catalonian: Anonymous
English: Deems Taylor, 1918
and Kurt Schindler, 1918

Anonymous

3. Guided by the wondrous ray
   Came three wise men holy,
   Where the Prince of Heaven lay
   In a manger lowly.
   Bringing Him, with joy untold,
   Frankincense and myrrh and gold,
   To the Holy Child, to the Mother mild.
   To the Child undefiled, in the arms of Mary,
   Blessed Virgin Mary.

4. Praise the day with joy and mirth,
   Love and exultation,
   When our Saviour came to earth,
   Bringing man salvation!
   Humble tho' our gift may be,
   Come we now on bended knee,
   With a heart so pure, with a heart so true,
   With a pure, with a true, with a deep emotion:
   All our hearts' devotion!

MEXICO

En Nombre Del Cielo

Open These Portals, I Pray

Mexican: Anonymous
English: Jane Flory, 1952

Anonymous

Allegretto

1.(Joseph) O - pen these por - tals, I pray, for the love of heav - en,
2.(Innkeeper) I do not o - pen to all who___ come___ knock - ing.

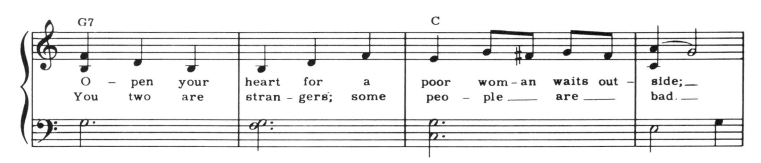

O - pen your heart for a poor wom - an waits out - side;___
You two are stran - gers; some peo - ple___ are___ bad.___

Wea - ry from trav - el, we seek here a place to rest, Please give us
There is no room here, so be on your way at once, On to an

lodg - ing for my wife___ can no long - er___ ride.___
inn where the lodg - ing___ you seek may be___ had.___

3. *(Joseph)*
All that I seek is a bed for my lovely wife.
All that I seek is a place where she can rest.
Can you not welcome the queen of heaven?
God will reward you! Your humble lodging will
be forever blest.

4. *(Innkeeper)*
Joseph and Mary come in, for I did not know you.
Enter my house; this night is one of joy!
Joy to the Mother so gracious and mild.
Lodging I give with my heart full of love for the
holy Child.

414-41072

GERMANY

O Tannenbaum

O Christmas Tree

German: Anonymous, 1820
English: George W. Anthony, 1966

Anonymous, 1799

1. O Christmas tree, O Christmas tree, So green through-out the sea - sons.

So green in sum - mer in the sun, And still as green in win ter's snow. O

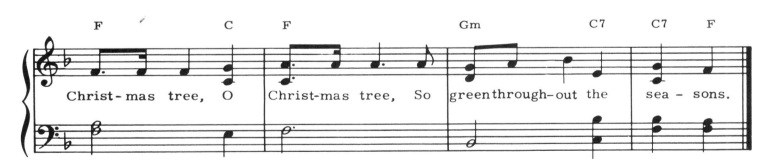

Christ-mas tree, O Christ-mas tree, So green through-out the sea - sons.

2.‖:O Christmas tree, O Christmas tree,
   Your beauty lasts forever.:‖
   But most of all at Christmastime
   Your boughs so rich bring joy sublime.
   O Christmas tree, O Christmas tree,
   Your beauty lasts forever.

3.‖:O Christmas tree, O Christmas tree,
   A lesson you can teach us.:‖
   You give us hope and constancy,
   And strengthen faith, O lovely tree.
   O Christmas tree, O Christmas tree,
   A lesson you can teach us.

414- 41072

UNITED STATES

Joy To The World

Isaac Watts, 1719
(1674-1748)

Lowell Mason, 1839
(1792-1872)

Allegro

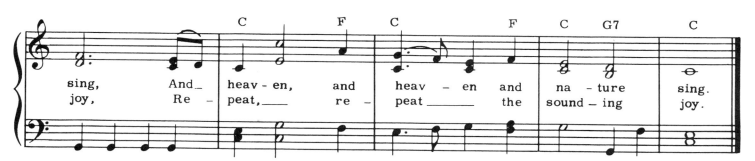

3. No more let sins and sorrows grow,
   Nor thorns infest the ground;
   He comes to make His blessings flow
   Far as the curse is found,
   Far as the curse is found,
   Far as, far as the curse is found.

4. He rules the world with truth and grace,
   And makes the nations prove
   The glories of His righteousness,
   And wonders of His love,
   And wonders of His love,
   And wonders, wonders of His love.

414- 41072

AUSTRIA

Stille Nacht, Heilige Nacht

Silent Night, Holy Night

German: Joseph Mohr, 1818
(1792-1848)

English: Anonymous, 1871

Franz X. Gruber, 1818
(1787-1863)

1. Si — lent night, ho — ly night, All is calm,
2. Si — lent night, ho — ly night, Shep — herds quake

all is bright Round yon Vir — gin Moth - er and Child.
at the sight, Glo — ries stream_ from heav - en a - far,

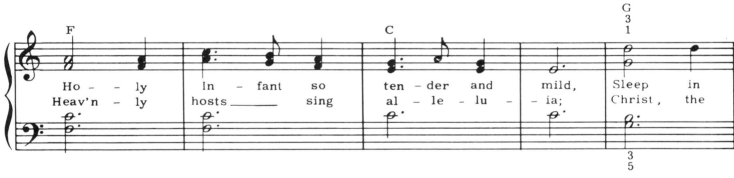

Ho — ly In — fant so ten - der and mild, Sleep in
Heav'n — ly hosts_____ sing al - le - lu — - ia; Christ, the

heav - en — ly peace,_____ Sleep in heav - en — ly peace.
Sav - iour, is born,_____ Christ, the Sav - iour, is born.

3. Silent night, holy night,
   Son of God, love's pure light
   Radiant beams from Thy holy face,
   With the dawn of redeeming grace,
   Jesus, Lord, at Thy birth,
   Jesus, Lord, at Thy birth.

4. Silent night, holy night,
   Wondrous star, lend thy light,
   With the angels let us sing,
   Alleluia to our King,
   Christ, the Saviour, is born,
   Christ, the Saviour, is born.

414- 41072

UNITED STATES

It Came Upon The Midnight Clear

Edmund H. Sears, 1846
(1810-1876)

Richard S. Willis, 1850
(1819-1900)

2. Still through the cloven skies they come
   With peaceful wings unfurled,
   And still their heavenly music floats
   O'er all the weary world;
   Above its sad and lowly plains
   They bend on hovering wing,
   And ever over its babel sounds
   The blessed angels sing.

3. Yet with the woes of sin and strife
   The world has suffered long;
   Beneath the heavenly strain have rolled
   Two thousand years of wrong;
   And man, at war with man, hears not
   The tidings which they bring;
   O hush the noise, ye men of strife,
   And hear the angels sing.

4. O ye, beneath life's crushing load,
   Whose forms are bending low,
   Who toil along the climbing way
   With painful steps and slow;
   Look now! for glad and golden hours
   Come swiftly on the wing;
   O rest beside the weary road
   And hear the angels sing.

5. For lo! the days are hastening on,
   By prophets seen of old,
   When with the ever-circling years
   Shall come the time foretold,
   When peace shall over all the earth
   Its ancient splendors fling,
   And the whole world give back the song
   Which now the angels sing.

ENGLAND

Now Sing We All Merrily

Anonymous

Welsh Tune: Anonymous

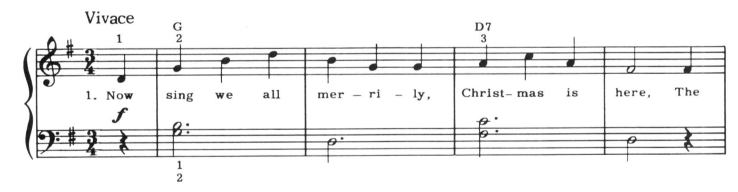

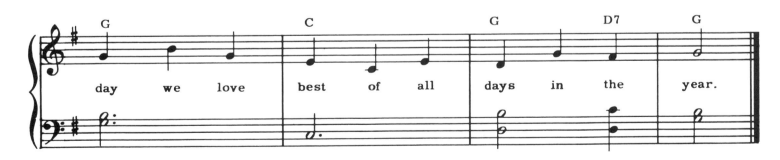

2. Bring out the green holly, the fir and the bay,
   And deck every cottage for glad Christmas Day.

3. The children are happy, with presents in hand,
   From Santa to children all over the land.

414-41072

GERMANY

Schönster Herr Jesu

Beautiful Saviour

German: Anonymous, 1677
English: Joseph A. Seiss, 1873
(1823-1904)

Anonymous, 1842

Andante

1. Beau - ti - ful Sav - iour, King of Cre - a - tion, Son of ___ God and ___ Son of Man! Tru - ly I'd love ___ Thee, Tru - ly I'd serve Thee, Light of my soul, my Joy, my Crown.

2. Fair are the meadows,
   Fair are the woodlands,
   Robed in flow'rs of blooming spring;
   Jesus is fairer,
   Jesus is purer;
   He makes our sorrowing spirit sing.

3. Beautiful Saviour,
   Lord of the nations,
   Son of God and Son of Man !
   Glory and honor,
   Praise, adoration,
   Now and forevermore be Thine !

414-41072

UNITED STATES

Away In A Manger

Anonymous

Anonymous

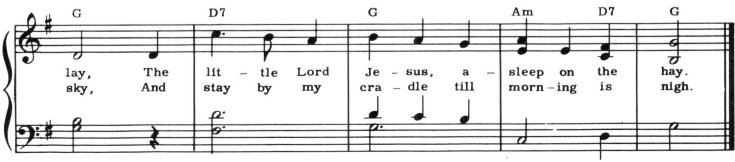

Andante

1. A - way in a man - ger, no crib for His
2. The cat - tle are low - ing, the Ba - by a -

bed, The lit - tle Lord Je - sus laid down His sweet
wakes, But lit - tle Lord Je - sus, no cry - ing he

head. The stars in the sky_____ look'd down where He
makes. I love Thee, Lord Je - sus, look down from the

lay, The lit - tle Lord Je - sus, a - sleep on the hay.
sky, And stay by my cra - dle till morn - ing is nigh.

414-41072

ENGLAND

Christians, Awake, Salute The Happy Morn

John Byrom, 1749
(1692-1763)

John Wainwright, 1750
(c.1723-1768)

414- 41072

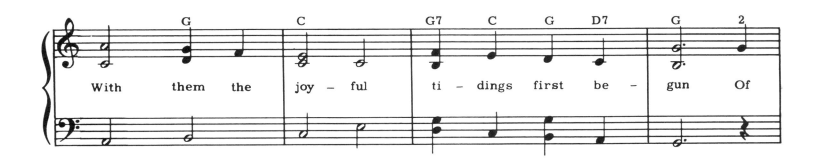

2. Then to the watchful shepherds it was told,
   Who heard the angelic herald's voice: "Behold,
   I bring good tidings of a Saviour's birth
   To you and all the nations on the earth:
   This day hath God fulfilled his promised word,
   This day is born a Saviour, Christ the Lord."

3. He spake, and straightway the celestial choir
   In hymns of joy, unknown before, conspire;
   The praises of redeeming love they sang,
   And heav'n's whole orb with alleluias rang;
   God's highest glory was their anthem still,
   Peace on the earth, and unto men good will.

4. To Bethl'hem straight the happy shepherds ran,
   To see the wonder God had wrought for man;
   And found, with Joseph and the blessed maid,
   Her Son, the Saviour, in a manger laid;
   Amazed, the wondrous story they proclaim,
   The earliest heralds of the Saviour's name.

5. Let us, like these good shepherds, then employ
   Our grateful voices to proclaim the joy;
   Trace we the Babe, who hath retrieved our loss,
   From his poor manger to his bitter cross;
   Treading his steps, assisted by his grace,
   Till man's first heav'nly state again takes place.

6. Then may we hope, the angelic thrones among,
   To sing, redeemed, a glad triumphal song;
   He that was born upon this joyful day
   Around us all his glory shall display;
   Saved by his love, incessant we shall sing
   Eternal praise to heav'n's Almighty King.

414-41072

ENGLAND

Deck The Hall

Anonymous, 1881

Welsh Tune: Anonymous, 1784

Vivace

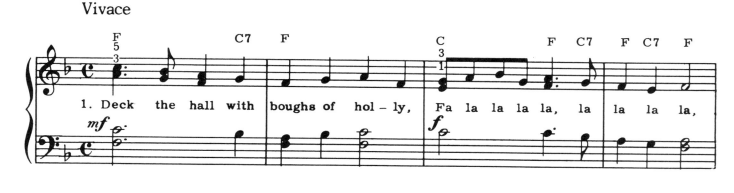

1. Deck the hall with boughs of hol – ly, Fa la la la la, la la la la,

'Tis the sea – son to be jol – ly, Fa la la la la, la la la la,

Don we now our gay ap – par – rel, Fa la la la la la, la la la,
cresc.

Troll the an – cient Christmas car – ol, Fa la la la la, la la la la.

2. See the blazing Yule before us,
   Fa la la la la, la la la la,
   Strike the harp and join the chorus,
   Fa la la la la, la la la la,
   Follow me in merry measure,
   Fa la la la la la, la la la,
   While I tell of Christmas treasure,
   Fa la la la la, la la la la.

3. Fast away the old year passes,
   Fa la la la la, la la la la,
   Hail the new! ye lads and lasses,
   Fa la la la la, la la la la,
   Sing we joyous all together,
   Fa la la la la la, la la la,
   Heedless of the wind and weather,
   Fa la la la la, la la la la.

ENGLAND

I Saw Three Ships

Anonymous   Anonymous

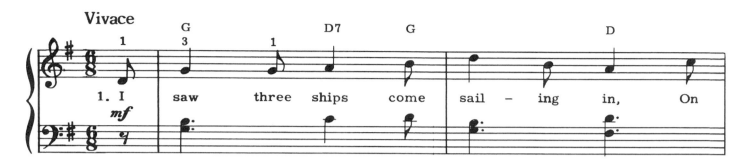

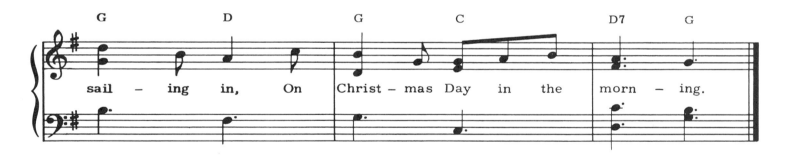

2. **And what was** in those ships all three,
   On Christmas Day, on Christmas Day?
   And what was in those ships all three,
   On Christmas Day in the morning?

3. **The Virgin Mary and Christ** were there,
   On Christmas Day, on Christmas Day;
   The Virgin Mary and Christ were there,
   On Christmas Day in the morning.

4. **O they** sailed into Bethlehem,
   On Christmas Day, on Christmas Day;
   O they sailed into Bethlehem,
   On Christmas Day in the morning.

5. And all the bells on earth shall ring
   On Christmas Day, on Christmas Day;
   And all the bells on earth shall ring
   On Christmas Day in the morning.

6. And all the souls on earth shall sing,
   On Christmas Day, on Christmas Day;
   And all the souls on earth shall sing,
   On Christmas Day in the morning.

7. Then let us all rejoice amain,
   On Christmas Day, on Christmas Day;
   Then let us all rejoice amain,
   On Christmas Day in the morning.

414-41072

ENGLAND

Good King Wenceslas

John M. Neale, 1853
(1818-1866)

Anonymous, 1582

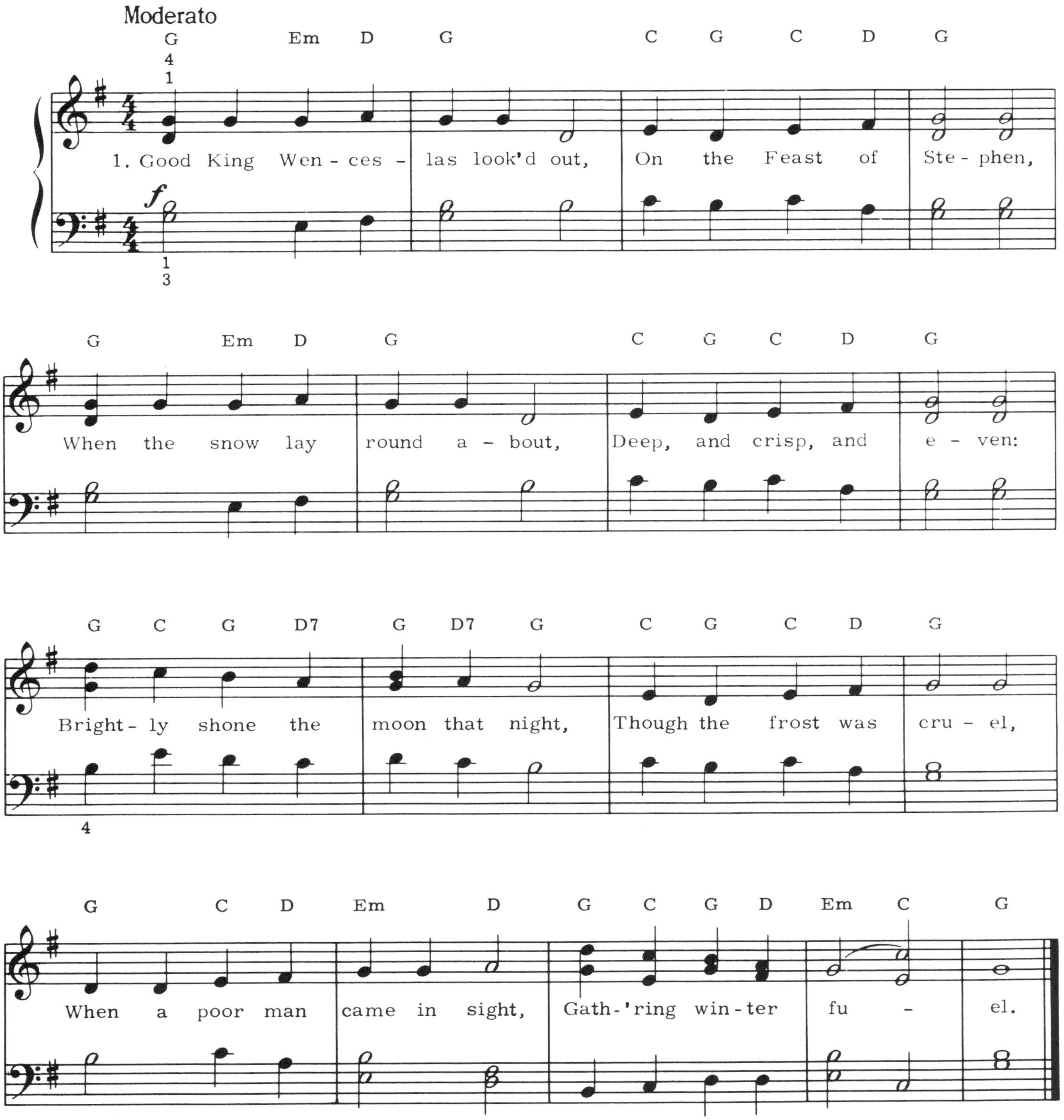

Moderato
G Em D G C G C D G
1. Good King Wen - ces - las look'd out, On the Feast of Ste - phen,
G Em D G C G C D G
When the snow lay round a - bout, Deep, and crisp, and e - ven:
G C G D7 G D7 G C G C D G
Bright - ly shone the moon that night, Though the frost was cru - el,
G C D Em D G C G D Em C G
When a poor man came in sight, Gath-'ring win - ter fu - el.

414-41072

2. "Hither, page, and stand by me,
   If thou know'st it, telling,
   Yonder peasant, who is he?
   Where and what his dwelling?"
   "Sire, he lives a good league hence,
   Underneath the mountain;
   Right against the forest fence,
   By Saint Agnes' fountain."

3. "Bring me flesh, and bring me wine,
   Bring me pine-logs hither:
   Thou and I will see him dine,
   When we bear them thither."
   Page and monarch, forth they went,
   Forth they went together;
   Through the rude wind's wild lament
   And the bitter weather.

4. "Sire, the night is darker now,
   And the wind blows stronger;
   Fails my heart, I know not how;
   I can go no longer."
   "Mark my footsteps, good my page;
   Tread thou in them boldly:
   Thou shalt find the winter's rage
   Freeze thy blood less coldly."

5. In his master's steps he trod,
   Where the snow lay dinted;
   Heat was in the very sod
   Which the Saint had printed.
   Therefore, Christian men, be sure,
   Wealth or rank possessing,
   Ye who now will bless the poor,
   Shall yourselves find blessing.

DENMARK

Det Kimer Nu Til Julefest

The Happy Christmas Comes Once More

Danish: Nicolai Grundtvig, 1817
English: Charles P. Krauth, 1867

C. Balle, 1850

2. To David's city let us fly,
   Where angels sing beneath the sky;
   Through plain and village pressing near,
   And news from God with shepherds hear.

3. O wake our hearts, in gladness sing,
   And keep our Christmas with our King,
   Till living song, from loving souls,
   Like sound of mighty water rolls!

414-41072

UNITED STATES

We Three Kings Of Orient Are

John H. Hopkins, 1857
(1820-1891)

John H. Hopkins, 1857
(1820-1891)

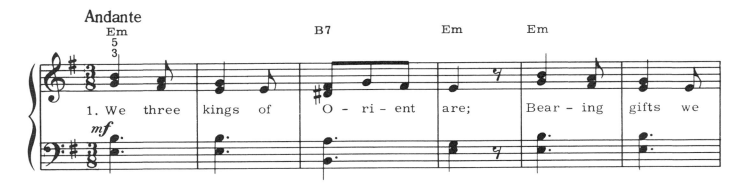

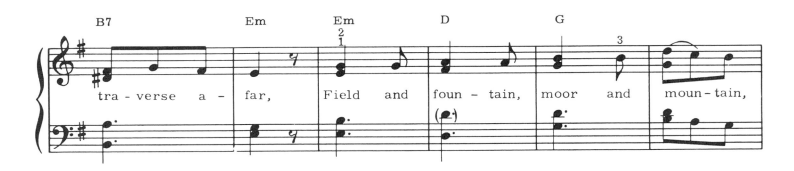

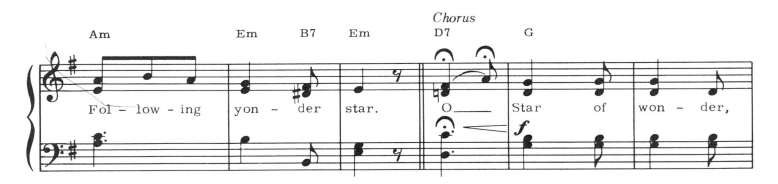

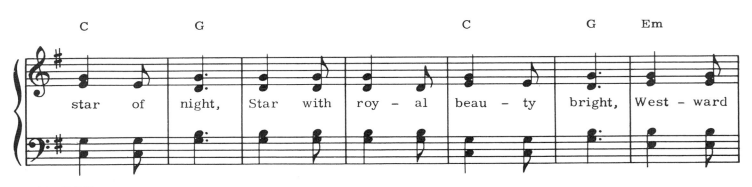

414-41072

© Copyright 1966 by Theodore Presser Co.

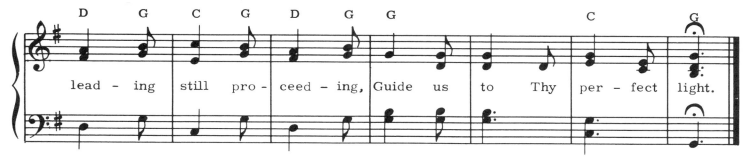

lead - ing still pro - ceed - ing, Guide us to Thy per - fect light.

2. Born a King on Bethlehem's plain,
   Gold I bring, to crown Him again,
   King forever, ceasing never,
   Over us all to reign.
   Chorus

3. Frankincense to offer have I,
   Incense owns a Deity nigh.
   Pray'r and praising, all men raising,
   Worship Him, God most High.
   Chorus

4. Myrrh is mine, its bitter perfume
   Breathes a life of gathering gloom;
   Sorrowing, sighing, bleeding, dying,
   Seal'd in the stone-cold tomb.
   Chorus

5. Glorious now behold Him arise,
   King and God and sacrifice,
   Alleluia, Alleluia;
   Earth to the heav'ns replies.
   Chorus

ENGLAND

Christ Was Born On Christmas Day

Anonymous

German Tune: Anonymous, 14th Century

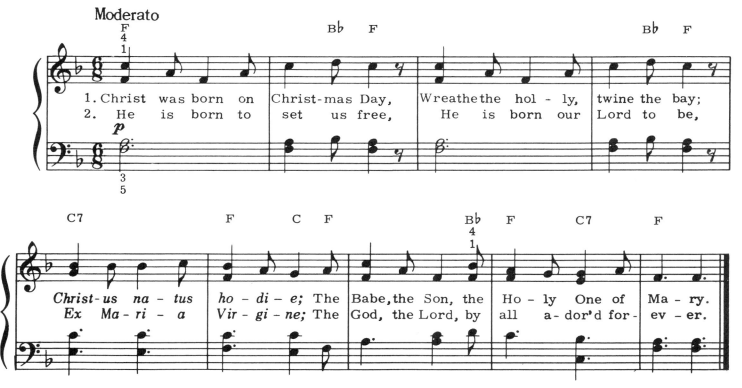

Moderato

1. Christ was born on Christ-mas Day, Wreathe the hol - ly, twine the bay;
2. He is born to set us free, He is born our Lord to be,

Christ-us na - tus ho - di - e; The Babe, the Son, the Ho - ly One of Ma - ry.
Ex Ma - ri - a Vir - gi - ne; The God, the Lord, by all a - dor'd for - ev - er.

3. Let the bright red berries glow,
   Everywhere in goodly show,
   Christus natus hodie;
   The Babe, the Son, the Holy One of Mary.

4. Christian men, rejoice and sing,
   'Tis the birthday of a King,
   Ex Maria Virgine;
   The God, the Lord, by all ador'd forever.

414-41072

UNITED STATES

Go Tell It On The Mountain

Anonymous

Anonymous

1. When I was a seek-er, I sought both night and day; I
2. He made me a watch-man Up-on the cit-y wall, And

asked the Lord to help me, And He showed me the way.___
if I am a Chris-tian, I am the least of all.___

Chorus

Go tell it on the moun-tain, O-ver the hills and ev-'ry-where;

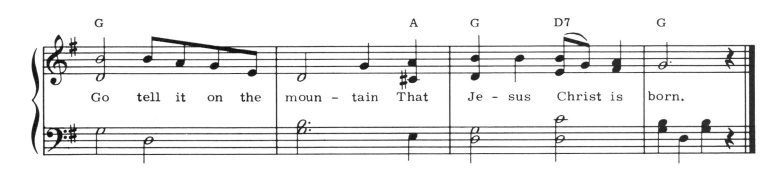

Go tell it on the moun-tain That Je-sus Christ is born.

414-41072

SPAIN

Fum, Fum, Fum

Fum, Fum, Fum

Catalonian: Anonymous
English: Marion Vree, 1955

Anonymous

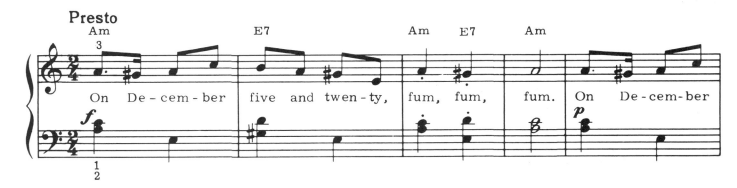

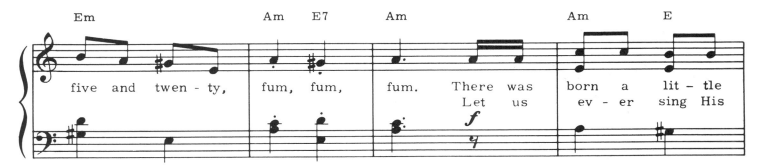

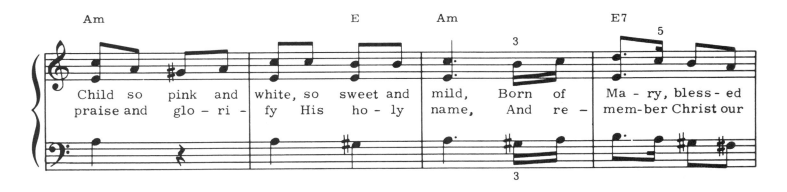

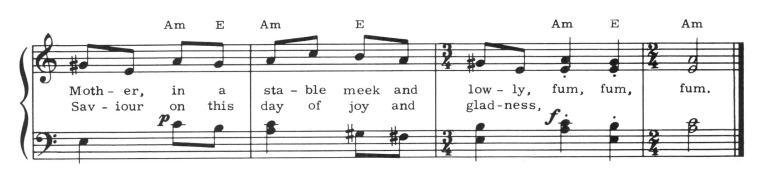

414-41072

ENGLAND

The First Nowell

Anonymous, 1833

Anonymous, 1833

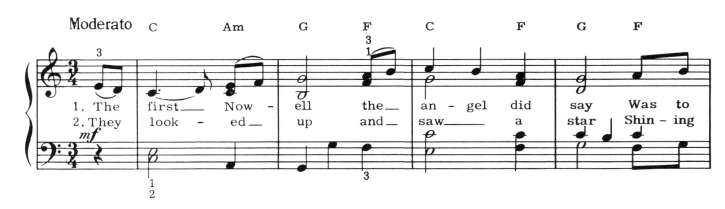

1. The first__ Now - ell the__ an - gel did say Was to
2. They look - ed__ up and__ saw_____ a star Shin - ing

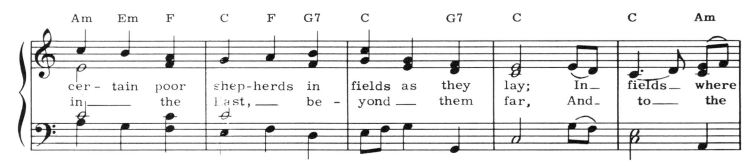

cer - tain poor shep-herds in fields as they lay; In__ fields__ where
in_____ the East,__ be - yond__ them far, And__ to__ the

they lay__ keep - ing their sheep On a cold win - ter's night____ that
earth it__ gave__ their great light, And__ so it con - tin - ued both

Chorus

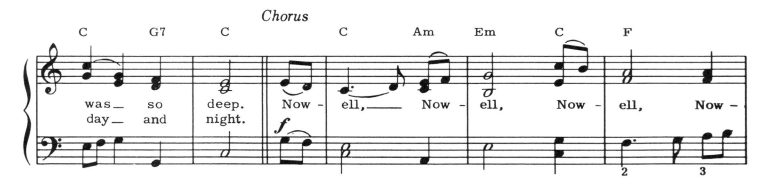

was__ so deep. Now - ell,____ Now - ell, Now - ell, Now -
day__ and night.

414-41072

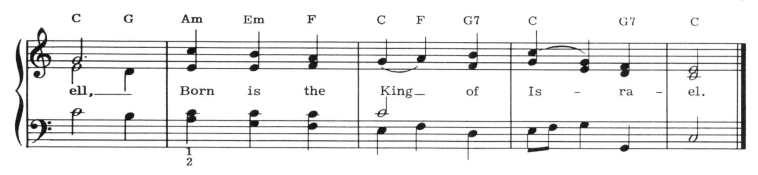

3. This star drew nigh to the Northwest,
   O'er Bethlehem it took its rest,
   And there it did both stop and stay
   Right over the place where Jesus lay.
   Chorus

4. Then enter'd in there Wise-men three,
   Full rev'rently upon their knee,
   And offer'd there in His presence,
   Their gold and myrrh and frankincense.
   Chorus

ENGLAND

Dame, Get Up And Bake Your Pies

Anonymous

Anonymous

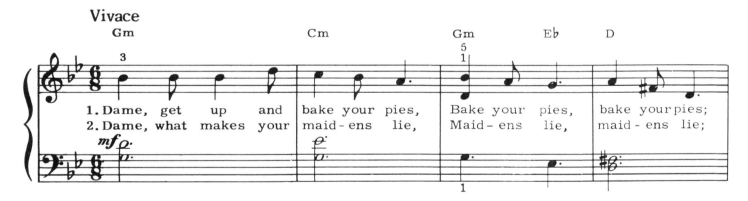

3. Dame, what makes your ducks to die,
   Ducks to die, ducks to die;
   Dame, what makes your ducks to die,
   On Christmas Day in the morning?

4. Their wings are cut and they cannot fly,
   Cannot fly, cannot fly;
   Their wings are cut and they cannot fly,
   On Christmas Day in the morning?

414-41072

ENGLAND

Good Christian Men, Rejoice

John M. Neale, 1853
(1818-1866)

Tune: In Dulci Jubilo, 14th Century

2. Good Christian men, rejoice
   With heart, and soul, and voice;
   Now ye hear of endless bliss:
   Jesus Christ was born for this!
   He hath ope'd the heav'nly door,
   And man is blessed evermore.
   Christ was born for this!
   Christ was born for this!

3. Good Christian men, rejoice
   With heart, and soul, and voice;
   Now ye need not fear the grave:
   Jesus Christ was born to save!
   Calls you one and calls you all
   To gain His everlasting hall.
   Christ was born to save!
   Christ was born to save!

414-41072

ENGLAND
The Holly And The Ivy

Anonymous, c.1700

Anonymous

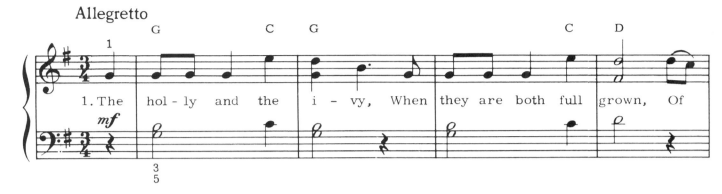

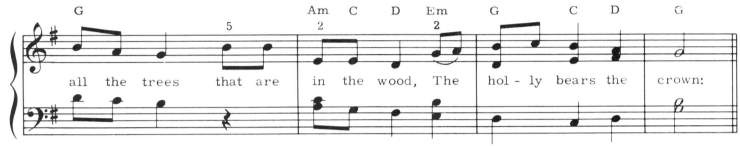

2. The holly bears a blossom,
   As white as the lily flower,
   And Mary bore sweet Jesus Christ,
   To be our sweet Saviour:
   Chorus

3. The holly bears a berry,
   As red as any blood,
   And Mary bore sweet Jesus Christ,
   To do poor sinners good:
   Chorus

4. The holly bears a prickle,
   As sharp as any thorn,
   And Mary bore sweet Jesus Christ,
   On Christmas Day in the morn:
   Chorus

5. The holly bears a bark,
   As bitter as any gall,
   And Mary bore sweet Jesus Christ,
   For to redeem us all:
   Chorus

414-41072

ENGLAND

Here We Come A-Wassailing

Anonymous

Anonymous, 19th Century

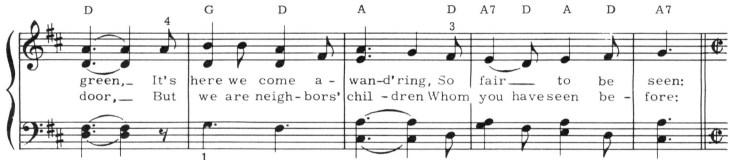

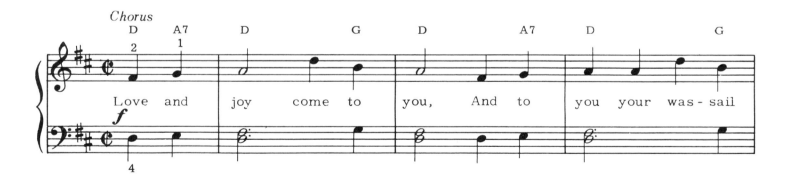

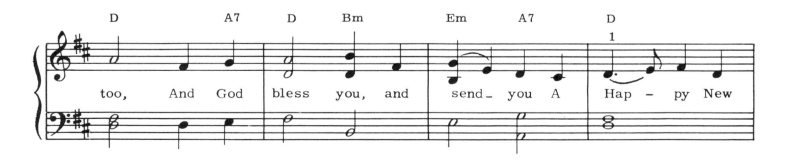

414-41072

3. Good master and good mistress,
   While you sit by fire,
   Pray think of us poor children
   Who wander in the mire:
   Chorus

4. God bless the master of this house,
   Likewise the mistress too;
   And all the little children
   That round the table go:
   Chorus

FRANCE

Quittez, Pasteurs

O Leave Your Sheep

French: Anonymous, 18th Century
English: George W. Anthony, 1966

Air from "Nanon Dormait," 1875

414-41072

UKRAINE

Christmas Bell Carol

English: George W. Anthony, 1966

Anonymous

414-41072

ENGLAND

The Holy Well

Anonymous

Anonymous

414-41072

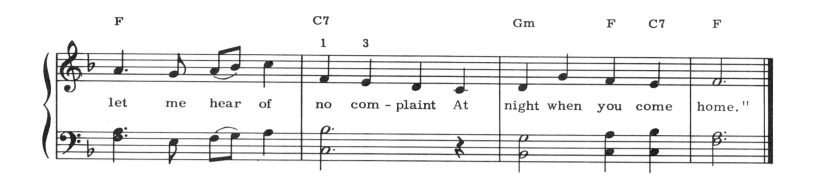

let me hear of no com - plaint At night when you come home."

2. Sweet Jesus went down to yonder town,
As far as the Holy Well,
And there did see as fine children
As any tongue can tell.
He said, "God bless you every one
And your bodies Christ save and see!
And now, little children, I'll play with you
And you shall play with me."

3. But they made answer to him, "No!
Thou art meaner than us all;
Thou art but a simple fair maid's child,
Born in an ox's stall."
Sweet Jesus turned him round about,
Neither laughed, nor smiled, nor spoke;
But the tears came trickling from his eyes
Like waters from the rock.

4. Sweet Jesus turned him round about,
To his mother's dear home went he,
And said, "I have been in yonder town,
As after you may see:
I have been down in yonder town,
As far as the Holy Well;
There did I meet with as fine children
As any tongue can tell.

5. I said, 'God bless you every one,
And your bodies Christ save and see!
And now, little children, I'll play with you
And you shall play with me.'
But they made answer to me, 'No!'
They were lords' and ladies' sons,
And I the meanest of them all,
Born in an ox's stall."

6. "Though you are but a maiden's child,
Born in an ox's stall,
Thou art the Christ, the King of Heaven,
And the Saviour of them all!
Sweet Jesus, go down to yonder town,
As far as the Holy Well,
And take away those sinful souls
And dip them deep in hell."

7. "Nay, nay," sweet Jesus smiled and said;
"Nay, nay, that may not be,
For there are too many sinful souls
Crying out for the help of me."
Then up spoke the angel Gabriel,
Upon a good set steven,
"Although you are but a maiden's child,
You are the King of Heaven!"

414- 41072

FRANCE

Les Anges Dans Nos Campagnes

Angels We Have Heard On High

French: Anonymous
English: Anonymous

Anonymous, 1855

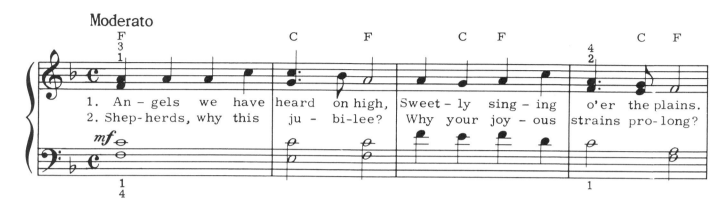

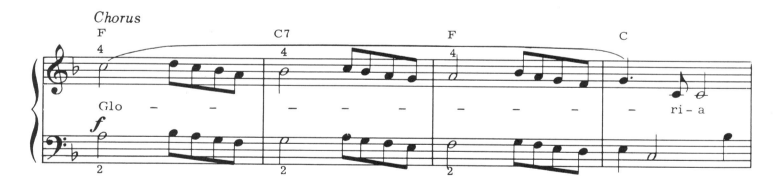

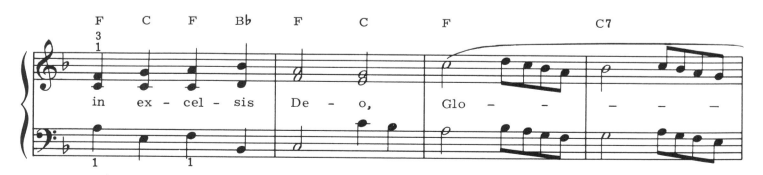

414-41072

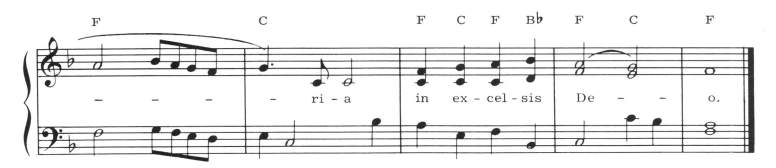

3. Come, to Bethlehem, and see
   Him whose birth the angels sing;
   Come, adore on bended knee,
   Christ the Lord, the new-born King.
   Chorus

4. See Him in the manger laid,
   Whom the choirs of angels praise;
   Mary, Joseph lend your aid,
   While our hearts in love we raise.
   Chorus

ENGLAND

Come, Thou Long-Expected Jesus

Charles Wesley, 1744
(1707-1788)

Melody adapted from Christian F. Witt, 1715
(1660-1716)

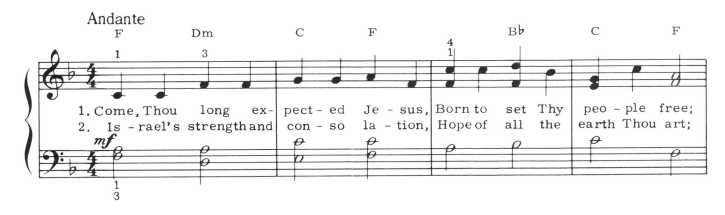

1. Come, Thou long ex-pect-ed Je-sus, Born to set Thy peo-ple free;
2. Is-rael's strength and con-so-la-tion, Hope of all the earth Thou art;

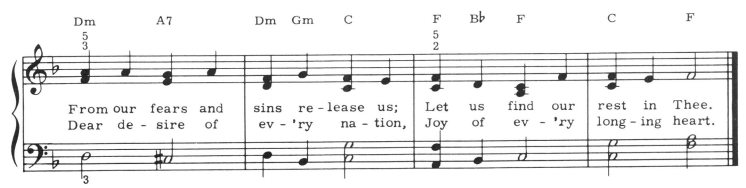

From our fears and sins re-lease us; Let us find our rest in Thee.
Dear de-sire of ev-'ry na-tion, Joy of ev-'ry long-ing heart.

3. Born Thy people to deliver,
   Born a child and yet a King,
   Born to reign in us forever,
   Now Thy gracious Kingdom bring.

4. By Thine own eternal Spirit
   Rule in all our hearts alone;
   By Thine all-sufficient merit
   Raise us to Thy glorious throne.

414-41072

ENGLAND

God Rest You Merry, Gentlemen

Anonymous, c.1770

Anonymous, 1827

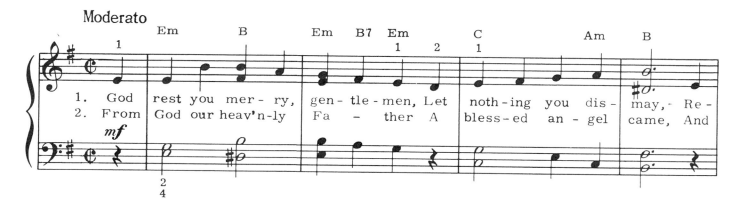

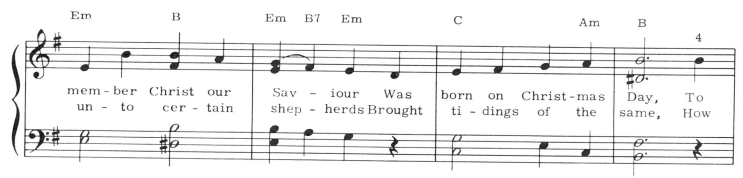

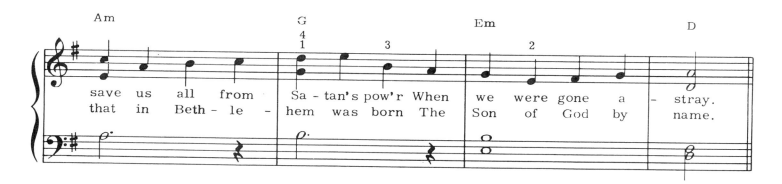

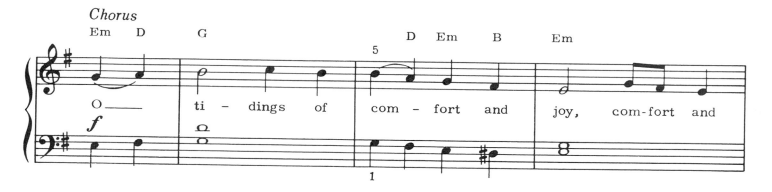

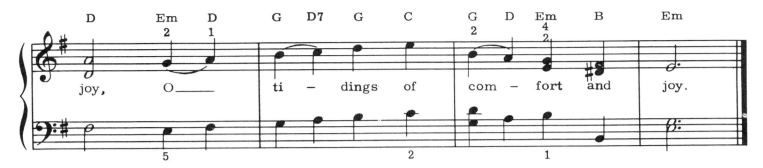

joy, O_____ ti - dings of com - fort and joy.

3. "Fear not," then said the angel,
   "Let nothing you affright,
   This day is born a Saviour
   Of a pure Virgin bright,
   To free all those who trust in Him
   From Satan's pow'r and might."
   Chorus

4. The shepherds at those tidings
   Rejoiced much in mind,
   And left their flocks a-feeding,
   In tempest, storm and wind;
   And went to Bethlehem straightway
   The Son of God to find.
   Chorus

5. And when they came to Bethlehem
   Where our dear Saviour lay,
   They found Him in a manger,
   Where oxen feed on hay;
   His mother Mary kneeling down,
   Unto the Lord did pray.
   Chorus

6. Now to the Lord sing praises,
   All you within this place,
   And with true love and brotherhood
   Each other now embrace;
   This holy tide of Christmas
   All other doth deface.
   Chorus

ENGLAND

Now Let Good Christians All Begin

Anonymous, 1822

Anonymous, 1822

Now__ let good Chris - tians all be - gin A ho - ly life to

live, And__ to re - joice and mer - ry be, For this is Christ-mas Eve.

414- 41072

ENGLAND

Let Christians All With Joyful Mirth

Anonymous

Anonymous

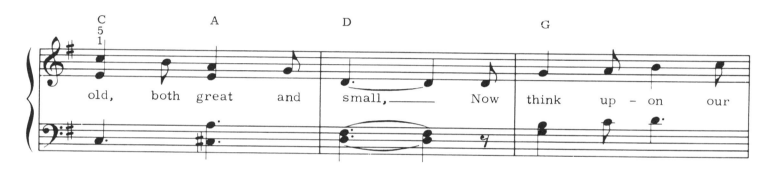

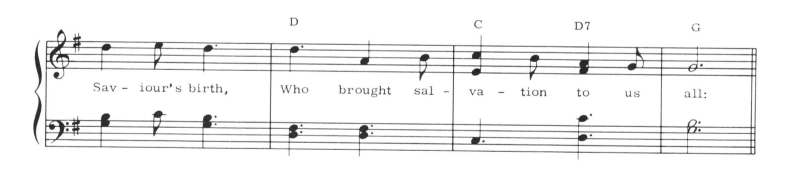

414- 41072

© Copyright 1966 by Theodore Presser Co.

With glo - rious saints to dwell in heav'n a - bove.——

2. No palace, but an ox's stall,
   The place of His nativity;
   This truly should instruct us all
   To learn of His humility:
   Chorus

3. Then Joseph and the Virgin came
   Unto the town of Bethlehem,
   But sought in vain within the same
   For lodging to be granted them:
   Chorus

4. A stable harboured them, where they
   Continued till this blessed morn.
   Let us rejoice and keep the day,
   Where-in the Lord of life was born:
   Chorus

5. He that descended from above,
   Who for your sins has meekly died,
   Make Him the pattern of your love:
   So will your joys be sanctified:
   Chorus

LATIN

Puer Nobis Nascitur

Unto Us Is Born A Son

Latin: Anonymous, 15th Century
English: Anonymous

Anonymous, 1582

1. Un - to us is born a Son, King of choirs su - per - nal: See on earth His life be - gun, Of lords the Lord e - ter - - - - - nal.

2. Christ, from heav'n descending low,
   Comes on earth a stranger:
   Ox and ass their Owner know
   Becradled in the manger.

3. Of His love and mercy mild
   This the Christmas story:
   O that Mary's gentle Child
   Might lead us up to glory!

414-41072

ENGLAND

When Christ Was Born Of Mary Free

Anonymous, 1456

Anonymous, 16th Century

2. The King is come to save mankind,
   As in the scripture truths we find,
   Therefore this song we have in mind,
   "In excelsis Gloria."
   Chorus

3. Then, dearest Lord, for Thy great grace,
   Grant us in bliss to see Thy face,
   That we may sing to Thy solace,
   "In excelsis Gloria."
   Chorus

414 - 41072

ENGLAND

Watchman, Tell Us Of The Night

John Bowring, 1825
(1792-1872)

George J. Elvey, 1859
(1816-1893)

2. Watchman, tell us of the night,
   Higher yet that star ascends:
   Traveler, blessedness and light,
   Peace and truth, its course portends.
   Watchman, will its beams alone
   Gild the spot that gave them birth?
   Traveler, ages are its own,
   And it bursts o'er all the earth!

3. Watchman, tell us of the night,
   For the morning seems to dawn:
   Traveler, darkness takes its flight;
   Doubt and terror are with-drawn.
   Watchman, let thy wanderings cease;
   Hie thee to thy quiet home.
   Traveler, lo, the Prince of Peace,
   Lo, the Son of God, is come!

414- 41072

ITALY

Canzone d'i Zampognari

When Christ Our Lord Was Born
(Carol Of The Bagpipers)

Sicilian: Anonymous
English: Theodore Baker, 1904
　　　　(1851-1934)

Anonymous

When　　Christ our Lord was　born ___ at　　Beth - le - hem ___ a

far, ___　Al - though 'twas night, there　shone ___ as ___ bright　as noon, a

star.　Nev - er　so　bright - ly, nev - er so　white - ly,　Shone the

stars, as　on ___ that　night! ___ The　bright - est　star ___　went　A -

way to call the Wise____ Men from the O - ri - ent.____

FRANCE

Aici L'estelo De Nadal

Whence Comes This Rush Of Wings Afar?
(Carol Of The Birds)

French: Anonymous
English: Anonymous

Anonymous

1. Whence comes this rush of wings a - far, Fol - lowing straight the No - el star?
2. "Tell us, — ye birds, why come ye here, In - to this sta - ble, poor and drear?"

Birds from the woods in won-drous flight, Beth - le -hem seek this ho - ly night.
"Hast-'ning we seek the new-born King, And all our sweet-est mu - sic bring."

3. Hark! how the green-finch bears his part,
Philomel, too, with tender heart,
Chants from her leafy dark retreat,
"Re, mi, fa, sol," in accents sweet.

4. Angels and shepherds, birds of the sky,
Come where the Son of God doth lie;
Christ on earth with man doth dwell,
Join in the shout, "Noel, Noel!"

414-41072

© Copyright 1966 by Theodore Presser Co.

ENGLAND

The Friendly Beasts

Anonymous   Anonymous, 12th Century

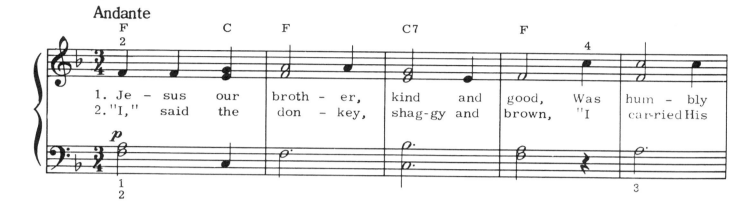

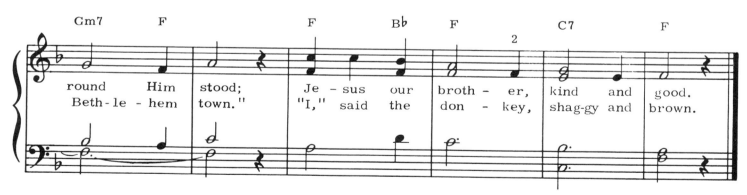

3. "I," said the cow all white and red,
   "I gave Him my manger for His bed,
   I gave Him my hay to pillow His head."
   "I," said the cow, all white and red.

4. "I," said the sheep with curly horn,
   "I gave Him my wool for His blanket warm,
   He wore my coat on Christmas morn."
   "I," said the sheep with curly horn.

5. "I," said the dove from the rafters high,
   "Cooed Him to sleep that He should not cry,
   We cooed Him to sleep, my mate and I."
   "I," said the dove from the rafters high.

6. Thus every beast by some good spell,
   In the stable dark was glad to tell
   Of the gift he gave Emmanuel,
   The gift he gave Emmanuel.

414-41072

ENGLAND

Hark! What Mean Those Holy Voices

John Cawood, 1819
(1775-1852)

Dmitri S. Bortniansky, 1818
(1751-1825)

1. Hark! what mean those ho - ly voi - ces, Sweet - ly sound - ing through the skies?
2. "Peace on earth, good - will from heav - en, Reach - ing far as man is found;

Lo! th'an - gel - ic host re - joi - ces, Heav'n - ly al - le - lu - ias rise.
Souls re - deemed and sins for - giv - en, Loud our gold - en harps shall sound."

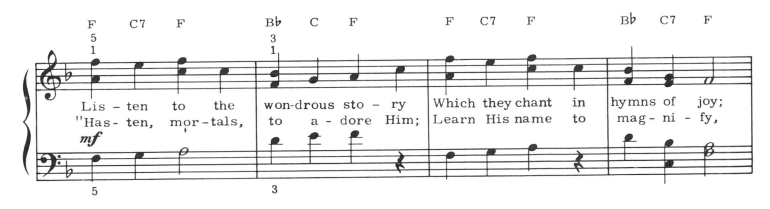

Lis - ten to the won - drous sto - ry Which they chant in hymns of joy;
"Has - ten, mor - tals, to a - dore Him; Learn His name to mag - ni - fy,

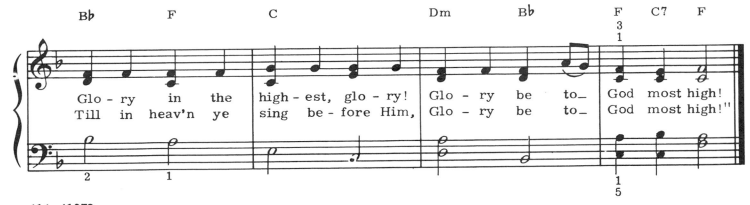

Glo - ry in the high - est, glo - ry! Glo - ry be to_ God most high!
Till in heav'n ye sing be - fore Him, Glo - ry be to_ God most high!"

414- 41072

FRANCE

Noël Nouvelet

Come, Good Christians All

French: Anonymous, c.1483
English: Charles F. Manney, 1918
    (1872-1951)

Anonymous

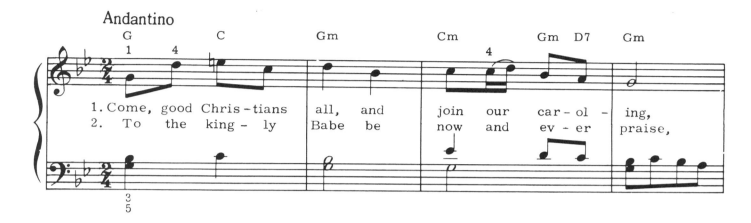

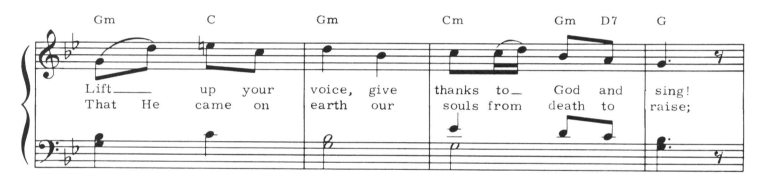

414-41072

Come, good Chris-tians all, and join our car-ol-ing!
Come, good Chris-tians all, and join our car-ol-ing!

UNITED STATES

Calm On The Listening Ear Of Night

Edmund H. Sears, 1835
(1810-1876)

John B. Dykes, 1866
(1823-1876)

1. Calm on the lis - t'ning ear of night
2. Ce - les - tial choirs from courts a - bove

Come heav'n's mel - o - dious strains, Where wild Ju - de - a
Shed sa - cred glo - ries there; And an - gels, with their

stretch - es far Her sil - ver - man - tled plains.
spark - ling lyres, Make mu - sic on the air.

3. "Glory to God!" the sounding skies
Loud with their anthems ring,
"Peace to the earth, good-will to men,
From heav'ns eternal King!"

4. Light on thy hills, Jerusalem!
The Saviour now is born;
More bright on Bethl'hem's joyous plains
Breaks the first Christmas morn.

414-41072

ENGLAND

Angels, From The Realms Of Glory

James Montgomery, 1816
(1771-1854)

Henry Smart, 1867
(1813-1879)

Tempo di Marcia

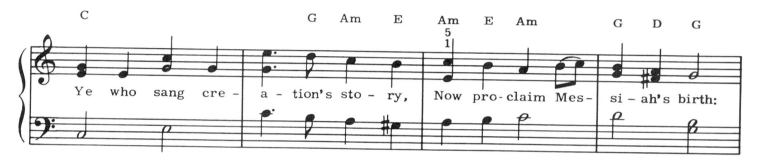

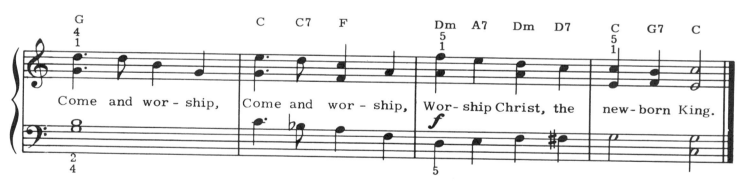

2. Shepherds, in the field abiding,
   Watching o'er your flocks by night,
   God with man is now residing;
   Yonder shines the infant Light:
   Come and worship,
   Come and worship,
   Worship Christ, the new-born King.

3. Sages, leave your contemplations,
   Brighter visions beam afar;
   Seek the great Desire of nations;
   Ye have seen His natal star:
   Come and worship,
   Come and worship,
   Worship Christ, the new-born King.

4. Saints, before the altar bending,
   Watching long in hope and fear,
   Suddenly the Lord, descending,
   In His temple shall appear:
   Come and worship,
   Come and worship,
   Worship Christ, the new-born King.

414-41072

ENGLAND

Ye Shepherds From The Mountains

Anonymous

French Tune: Anonymous

1. Ye shepherds from the moun-tains, Come down to us this morn! With-
2. Fair Beth-l'em is the vil-lage Which has the In-fant dear; Be-

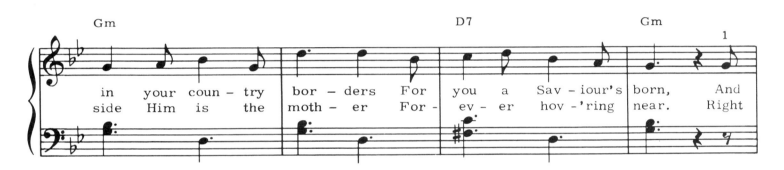

in your coun – try bor – ders For you a Sav – iour's born, And
side Him is the moth – er For – ev – er hov –'ring near. Right

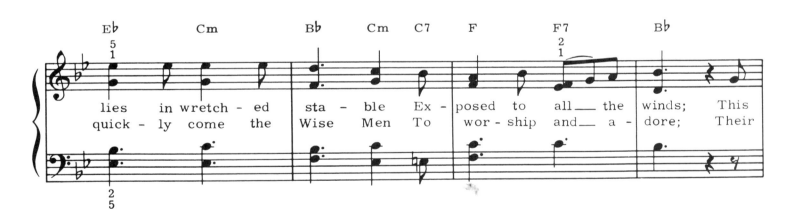

lies in wretch – ed sta – ble Ex – posed to all __ the winds; This
quick – ly come the Wise Men To wor – ship and __ a – dore; Their

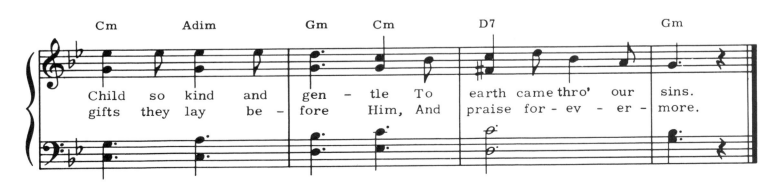

Child so kind and gen – tle To earth came thro' our sins.
gifts they lay be – fore Him, And praise for – ev – er – more.

414- 41072

© Copyright 1966 by Theodore Presser Co.

FRANCE

Un Flambeau, Jeannette, Isabelle

Bring A Torch, Jeannette, Isabella

French: Emile Blémont
English: E. Cuthbert Nunn
(1868-1914)

Anonymous, 17th Century

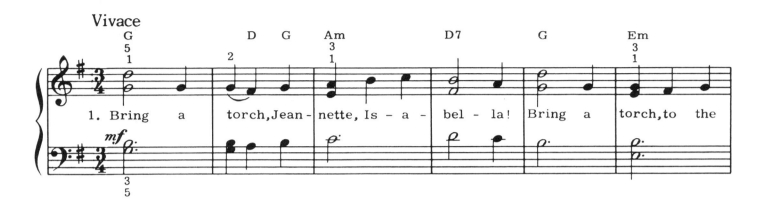

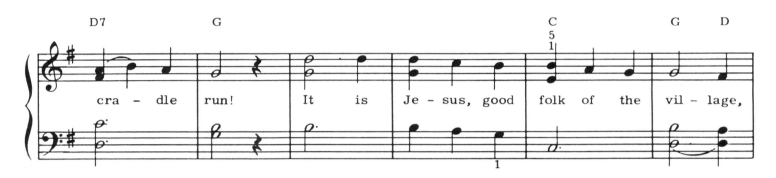

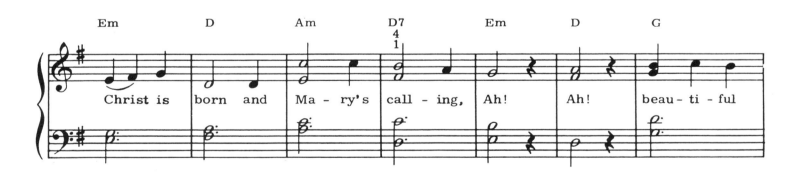

414-41072

2. It is wrong when the Child is sleeping,
   It is wrong to talk so loud.
   Silence, all, as you gather around,
   Lest your noise should waken Jesus:
   Hush! Hush! see how fast He slumbers;
   Hush! Hush! see how fast He sleeps!

3. Softly to the little stable,
   Softly for a moment come!
   Look and see how charming is Jesus,
   How He is white, His cheeks are rosy!
   Hush! Hush! see how the Child is sleeping;
   Hush! Hush! see how He smiles in dreams!

ENGLAND

Songs Of Praise The Angels Sang

James Montgomery, 1823
(1771-1854)

Anonymous, 13th Century

2. Songs of praise awoke the morn
   When the Prince of Peace was born;
   Songs of praise arose when He
   Captive led captivity.

3. Heav'n and earth must pass away;
   Songs of praise shall crown that day.
   God will make new heav'ns and earth;
   Songs of praise whall hail their birth.

4. Saints below, with heart and voice,
   Still in songs of praise rejoice;
   Learning here, by·faith and love,
   Songs of praise to sing above.

5. Borne upon their latest breath,
   Songs of praise shall conquer death;
   Then, amidst eternal joy,
   Songs of praise their powers employ.

414-41072

ENGLAND

Ding Dong! Merrily On High

Anonymous

French Dance: Anonymous, **1588**

1. Ding dong! mer-ri-ly on high The bells are gai-ly ring-ing;
2. Ding dong! car-ol all the bells, A-wake now, do not tar-ry!

Ding dong! hap-pi-ly re-ply, The an-gels all a-sing-ing.
Sing out, sound the good now-ells, Je-su is born of Ma-ry.

Chorus

Glo — — — — — — — — — — — — — — —

— — — — ri-a Ho-san-na in ex-cel-sis.

3. Ring out, merry, merry bells,
   The angels all are singing;
   Ding dong! swing the steeple bells,
   Sound joyous news we're bringing!
   Chorus

4. Hark now! happily we sing,
   The angels wish us merry!
   Ding dong! dancing as we bring
   Good news from Virgin Mary.
   Chorus

414-41072

POLAND

W Zlobie Lezy

Infant In The Manger

Polish: Anonymous
English: Roberta Carlson, 1966

Anonymous, 13th Century

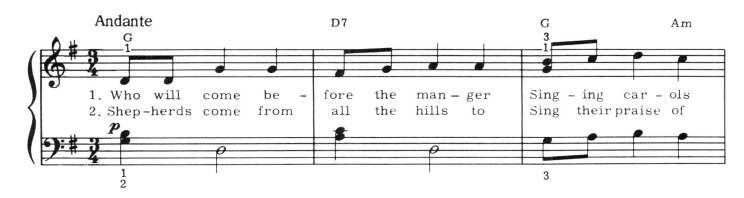

414-41072

ENGLAND

Come, Ye Lofty, Come, Ye Lowly

Archer Gurney
(1820-1887)

Anonymous

2. Come, ye poor, no pomp of station
Robes the Child your hearts adore:
He, the Lord of all salvation,
Shares your want, is weak and poor:
Oxen, round about behold them;
Rafters naked, cold, and bare,
See the shepherds, God has told them
That the Prince of Life lies there.

3. Come, ye children, blithe and merry,
This one Child your model make;
Christmas holly, leaf and berry,
All be prized for His dear sake;
Come, ye gentle hearts and tender,
Come, ye spirits keen and bold,
All in all your homage render,
Weak and mighty, young and old.

ENGLAND

As With Gladness Men Of Old

William C. Dix, 1860
(1837-1898)

Arr. from Conrad Kocher, 1861
(1786-1872)

3. As they offer'd gifts most rare
At that manger rude and bare,
So may we with holy joy,
Pure, and free from sin's alloy,
All our costliest treasures bring,
Christ, to Thee, our heavenly King.

4. Holy Jesus, every day
Keep us in the narrow way;
And, when earthly things are past,
Bring our ransomed souls at last
Where they need no star to guide,
Where no clouds Thy glory hide.

414-41072

Berger, Secoue Ton Sommeil Profond

Shepherds! Shake Off Your Drowsy Sleep

French: Anonymous
English: Anonymous

Anonymous

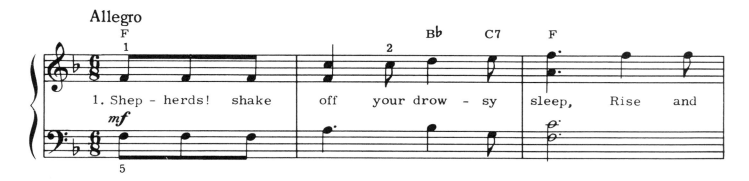

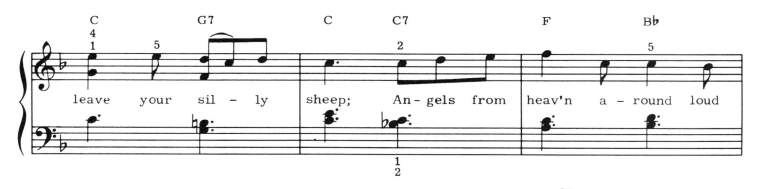

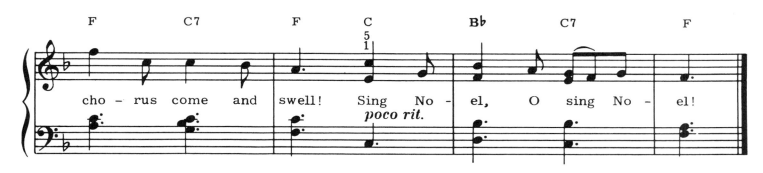

2. Cometh at length the age of peace,
   Strife and sorrow now shall cease;
   Prophets foretold the wondrous story
   Of this heav'n-born Prince of Glory.
   Chorus

3. Shepherds! then up and quick away,
   Seek the Babe ere break of day;
   He is the hope of ev'ry nation,
   All in Him shall find salvation.
   Chorus

414-41072

FRANCE

Quoique Soyez Petit Encore

Though Thou Art Now An Infant Small

French: Anonymous, 18th Century
English: Charles F. Manney, 1918
(1872-1951)

Anonymous, 18th Century

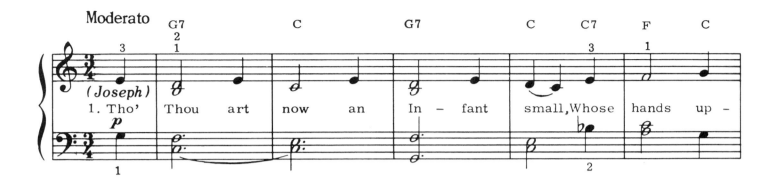

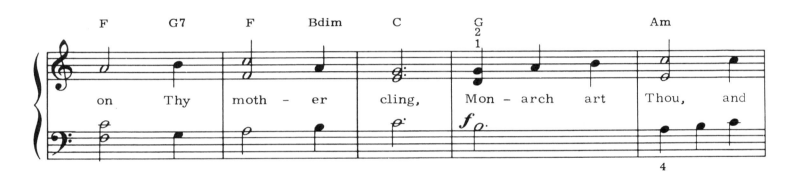

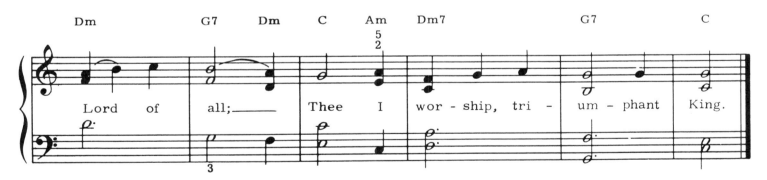

2. *(Shepherds)*
What wondrous thing is this we see,
A Babe with pow'r beyond compare!
Yonder Child on Mary's knee
Is the Lord of earth and air.

3. *(Joseph)*
Ye who are fired by holy zeal,
Draw near in faith and greet the Child;
At His cradle humbly kneel
To receive His blessing mild.

4. *(Shepherds)*
We are but poor, no gifts have we
To fill Thy hands so fair and small,
But for love, dear Babe, of Thee,
We will love our brothers all.

5. *(Shepherds)*
Sleep on in peace and take Thy rest,
True Son of God, with us to dwell:
We will spread the tidings blest,
After singing our glad Noel.

414-41072

ENGLAND

The Virgin Stills The Crying

Anonymous   Anonymous

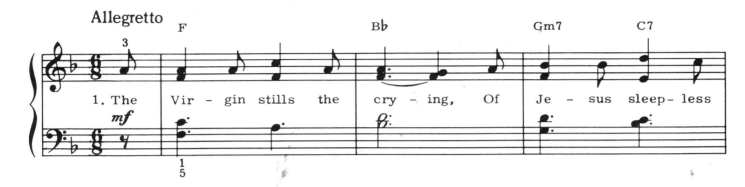

1. The Vir - gin stills the cry - ing, Of Je - sus sleep-less

ly - ing, And sing - ing for His pleas - ure, Thus calls up - on her

trea - sure,— My dar - ling, do not weep, My Je - sus sleep, sleep!

2. O lamb, my love inviting,
   O star, my soul delighting,
   O flow'r of mine own bearing,
   O jewel past comparing!
   My darling, do not weep,
   My Jesus, sleep, sleep!

3. My Child of might in dwelling,
   My sweet, all sweet excelling,
   Of bliss the fountain flowing,
   The day spring ever glowing.
   My darling, do not weep,
   My Jesus, sleep, sleep!

4. My joy, my exultation,
   My spirit's consolation,
   My son, my spouse, my brother,
   O listen to Thy Mother!
   My darling, do not weep,
   My Jesus, sleep, sleep!

5. Say, wouldst Thou heav'nly sweetness,
   Or love of answ'ring meetness?
   Or is fit music wanting?
   Ho! angels, raise your chanting!
   My darling, do not weep,
   My Jesus, sleep, sleep!

414-41072

ENGLAND

Lullay, Thou Little Tiny Child
(The Coventry Carol)

Robert Croo, 1534

Anonymous, 1591

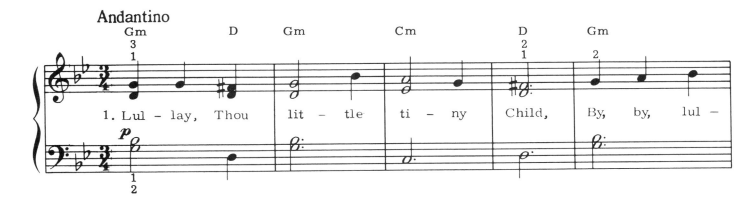

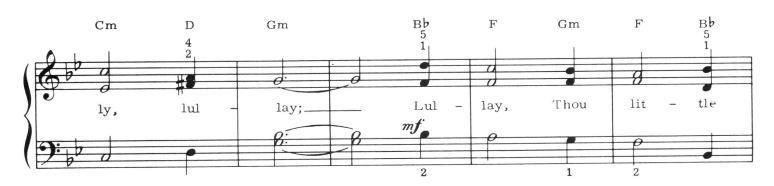

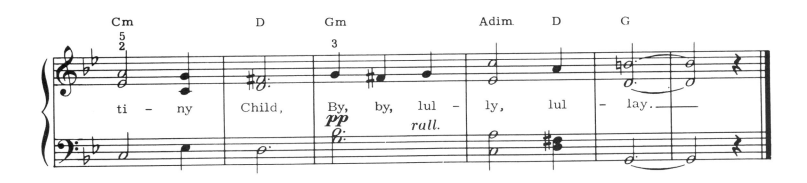

2. O sisters, too, how may we do
   For to preserve this day;
   This poor Youngling for whom we sing,
   By, by, lully, lullay?

3. Herod the king, in his raging,
   Charged he hath this day,
   His men of might in his own sight
   All children young to slay.

4. Then woe is me, poor Child, for Thee,
   And ever morn and day;
   For Thy parting nor say nor sing,
   By, by, lully, lullay.

414-41072

ENGLAND

God Give Ye Merry Christmastide

Anonymous

Anonymous

414 - 41072

2. Ye hang the twining winter-green,
   The glad home-fires ye light,
   And cheery Merry Christmas keep,
   With hearts and voices bright.
   But in a stall at Bethlehem,
   Where simple shepherds pray,
   Chorus

3. God give ye merry Christmastide,
   And give ye all to see
   How blessed 'tis to give and know
   The grace of charity.
   Rejoice! for once at Bethlehem,
   To give His life away,
   Chorus

AUSTRIA

Still, Still, Still

Hush, Now Hush

Austrian: Anonymous
English: George W. Anthony, 1966

Anonymous, 1819

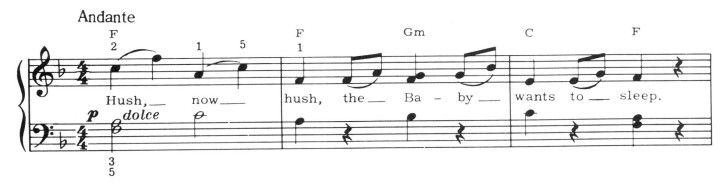

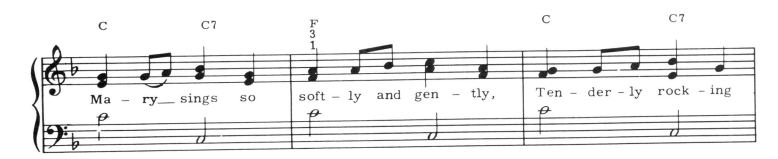

414-41072

UNITED STATES

The Birthday Of A King

William H. Neidlinger, 1890
(1863-1924)

William H. Neidlinger, 1890
(1863-1924)

1. In the lit - tle vil - lage of Beth - le - hem, There lay a Child one day, And the sky was bright with a ho - ly light, O'er the place where Je - sus lay: Al - le - lu - ia! O how the an - gels sang, Al - le - lu - ia! how it rang; And the

2. 'Twas a hum - ble birthplace, but oh! how much God gave to us that day, From the man - ger bed, what a path has led What a per - fect ho - ly way: Al - le - lu - ia! O how the an - gels sang, Al - le - lu - ia! how it rang; And the

sky was bright with a ho — ly light, 'Twas the birth — day of a King.
sky was bright with a ho — ly light, 'Twas the birth — day of a King.

ENGLAND

A Babe Is Born All Of A Maid

Anonymous, 15th Century

Anonymous

1. A Babe is born all of a maid, To
2. At Beth — le — hem, that bless — ed place, The

bring sal — va — tion un — to__ us. To
Child of bliss now born He__ was; And

Him we sing both night and__ day, *Ve — ni cre — a — tor Spi — ri — tus.*
Him to serve God give us__ grace, *O lux__ bea — ta Trin — i — tas.*

3. There came three kings out of the East,
   To worship the King that is so free,
   With gold and myrrh and frankincense,
   A solis ortus cardine.

4. The angels came down with one cry,
   A fair song that night sung they
   In the worship of that Child,
   Gloria tibi Domine.

414- 41072

VENEZUELA

Como Busca El Tierno Infante

As The Tender Baby Jesus

Venezuelan: Anonymous
English: Sybil Reid, 1966

Anonymous

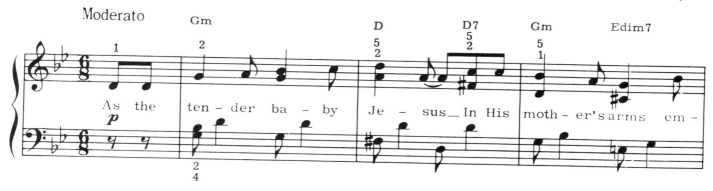

As the ten – der ba – by Je – sus In His moth – er's arms em –

braced,___ Sought her warm and sweet af – fec – tion___ In that

cold and dis – tant place, So do I, my heav'n – ly

la – dy, Come to you to seek and plea:___ O please

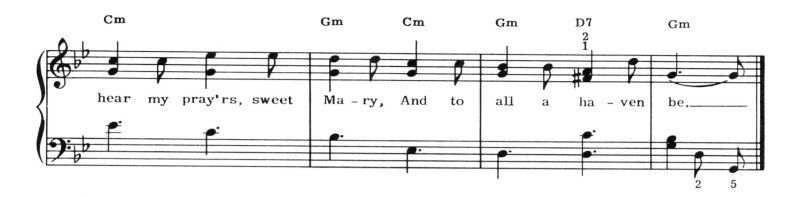

hear my pray'rs, sweet Ma - ry, And to all a ha - ven be.____

ENGLAND

A Child This Day Is Born

Anonymous, 1833   Anonymous, 1833

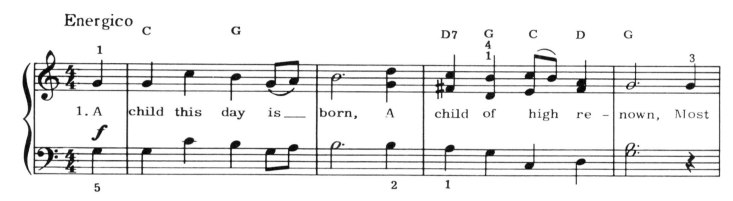

Energico

1. A child this day is___ born, A child of high re - nown, Most

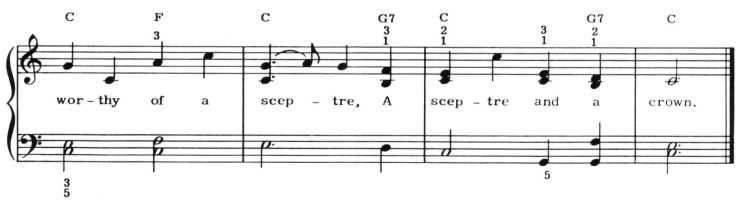

wor - thy of a scep - tre, A scep - tre and a crown.

2. These tidings shepherds heard,
In field watching their fold,
Were by an angel unto them
That night revealed and told.

3. To whom the angel spoke,
Saying, "Be not afraid;
Be glad, poor silly shepherds,
Why are you so dismayed?

4. For lo! I bring you tidings
Of gladness and of mirth,
Which cometh to all people by
This holy infant's birth."

5. And as the angel told them,
So to them did appear;
They found the young child, Jesus Christ
With Mary, his mother dear.

414-41072

© Copyright 1966 by Theodore Presser Co.

GERMANY

Der Christbaum Ist Der Schönste Baum

The Most Beautiful Tree

German: Anonymous
English: George W. Anthony, 1966

Anonymous

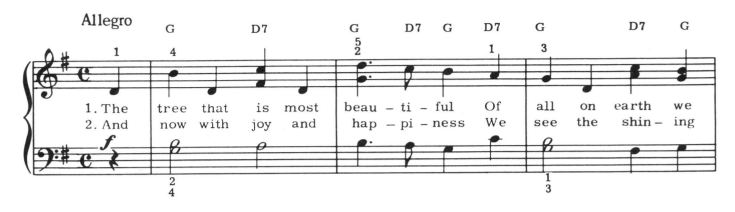

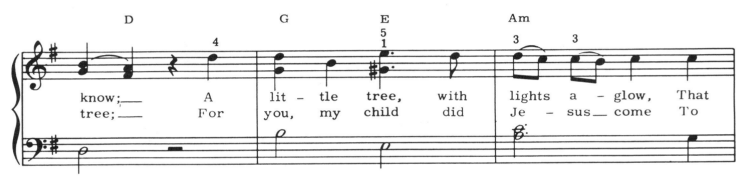

414- 41072

El Rorro
The Babe
(The Rocking Carol)

Mexican: Anonymous
English: Jane Flory, 1952

Anonymous

414-41072

CANADA

D'où Viens-Tu, Bergère?

Whence Art Thou, My Maiden?

French Canadian: Anonymous
English: William McLennan, 1866

Anonymous

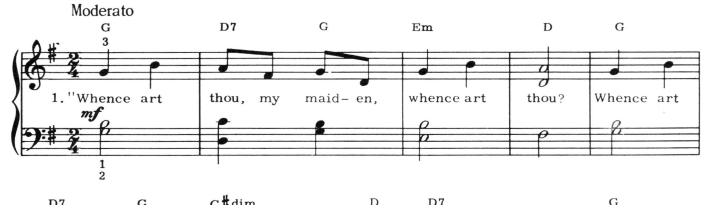

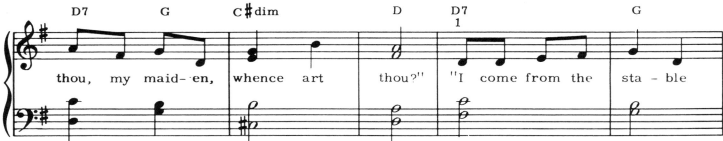

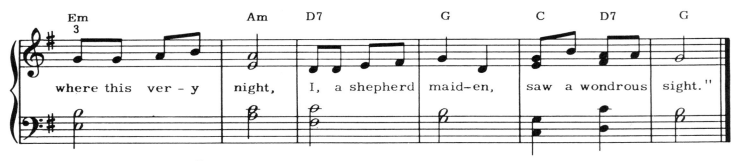

2. "What saw'st thou, my maiden, what saw'st thou?
   What saw'st thou, my maiden, what saw'st thou?"
   "There within a manger, a little Child I saw
   Lying, softly sleeping, on a bed of straw."

3. "Nothing more, my maiden, nothing more?
   Nothing more, my maiden, nothing more?"
   "There I saw the mother her sweet Baby hold,
   And the father, Joseph, trembling with the cold."

4. "Nothing more, my maiden, nothing more?
   Nothing more, my maiden, nothing more?"
   "I saw ass and oxen, kneeling meek and mild,
   With their gentle breathing warm the holy Child."

5. "Nothing more, my maiden, nothing more?
   Nothing more, my maiden, nothing more?"
   "There were three bright angels come down from the sky,
   Singing forth sweet praises to our God on high."

414-41072

What Child is This?

1. What Child is this, Who, laid to rest
    On Mary's lap is sleeping?
    Whom angels greet with anthems sweet,
    While shepherds watch are keeping?
    This, this is Christ the King,
    Whom shepherds guard and angels sing:
    Haste, haste to bring Him laud,
    The Babe, the Son of Mary!

2. So bring Him incense, gold and myrrh,
    Come peasant, King, to own Him,
    The King of kings salvation bring,
    Let loving hearts enthrone Him.
    Raise, raise the song on high,
    The virgin sings her lullaby:
    Joy, joy for Christ is born,
    The Babe, the Son of Mary

The First Nowell

1. The first Nowell the angel did say
    Was to certain poor shepherds, in fields as they lay,
    In fields where they lay keeping their sheep,
    On a cold winter's night that was so deep.
    Nowell, Nowell, Nowell, Nowell,
    Born is the King of Israel.

2. They looked up and saw a star,
    Shining in the east beyond them far,
    And to the earth it gave great light,
    And so it continued both day and night. *Nowell, ...*

3. And by the light of that same star,
    Three wise men came from country far;
    To seek for a king was their intent,
    And to follow the star where-ever it went. *Nowell ...*

4. Then entered in those wise men three,
    Most reverently upon their knee,
    And offered there, in his presence,
    Both gold and myrrh and frankincense. *Nowell, ...*

Angels We Have Heard on High

1. Angels we have heard on high
    Sweetly singing through the night,
    And the mountains in reply
    Echoing their brave delight.
    Gloria in excelsis Deo. Gloria in excelsis Deo.

2. Shepherds, why this jubilee?
    Why these songs of happy cheer?
    What great brightness did you see?
    What glad tidings did you hear?
    Gloria...

3. Come to Bethlehem and see
    Him whose birth the angels sing;
    Come, adore on bended knee,
    Christ, the Lord, the newborn King.
    Gloria...

Silent Night

1. Silent night, holy night,
    All is calm, all is bright
    Round yon virgin mother and child
    Holy infant so tender and mild,
    Sleep in heavenly peace,
    Sleep in heavenly peace.

2. Silent night, holy night,
    Shepherds quake at the sight,
    Glories stream from heaven afar,
    Heavenly hosts sing "Alleluia,
    Christ, the Savior is born!
    Christ, the Savior is born!"

3. Silent night, holy night,
    Son of God, love's pure light
    Radiant beams from thy holy face,
    With the dawn of redeeming grace,
    Jesus, Lord, at thy birth,
    Jesus, Lord, at thy birth.

Hanerot

What Child is This?

1. What Child is this, Who, laid to rest
   On Mary's lap is sleeping?
   Whom angels greet with anthems sweet,
   While shepherds watch are keeping?
   This, this is Christ the King,
   Whom shepherds guard and angels sing:
   Haste, haste to bring Him laud,
   The Babe, the Son of Mary!

2. So bring Him incense, gold and myrrh,
   Come peasant, King, to own Him,
   The King of kings salvation bring,
   Let loving hearts enthrone Him.
   Raise, raise the song on high,
   The virgin sings her lullaby:
   Joy, joy for Christ is born,
   The Babe, the Son of Mary

The First Nowell

1. The first Nowell the angel did say
   Was to certain poor shepherds, in fields as they lay,
   In fields where they lay keeping their sheep,
   On a cold winter's night that was so deep.
   Nowell, Nowell, Nowell, Nowell,
   Born is the King of Israel.

2. They looked up and saw a star,
   Shining in the east beyond them far,
   And to the earth it gave great light,
   And so it continued both day and night. *Nowell, ...*

3. And by the light of that same star,
   Three wise men came from country far;
   To seek for a king was their intent,
   And to follow the star where-ever it went. *Nowell ...*

4. Then entered in those wise men three,
   Most reverently upon their knee,
   And offered there, in his presence,
   Both gold and myrrh and frankincense. *Nowell, ...*

Angels We Have Heard on High

1. Angels we have heard on high
   Sweetly singing through the night,
   And the mountains in reply
   Echoing their brave delight.
   Gloria in excelsis Deo. Gloria in excelsis Deo.

2. Shepherds, why this jubilee?
   Why these songs of happy cheer?
   What great brightness did you see?
   What glad tidings did you hear?
   Gloria...

3. Come to Bethlehem and see
   Him whose birth the angels sing;
   Come, adore on bended knee,
   Christ, the Lord, the newborn King.
   Gloria...

Silent Night

1. Silent night, holy night,
   All is calm, all is bright
   Round yon virgin mother and child
   Holy infant so tender and mild,
   Sleep in heavenly peace,
   Sleep in heavenly peace.

2. Silent night, holy night,
   Shepherds quake at the sight,
   Glories stream from heaven afar,
   Heavenly hosts sing "Alleluia,
   Christ, the Savior is born!
   Christ, the Savior is born!"

3. Silent night, holy night,
   Son of God, love's pure light
   Radiant beams from thy holy face,
   With the dawn of redeeming grace,
   Jesus, Lord, at thy birth,
   Jesus, Lord, at thy birth.

Hanerot

What Child is This?

1. What Child is this, Who, laid to rest
   On Mary's lap is sleeping?
   Whom angels greet with anthems sweet,
   While shepherds watch are keeping?
   This, this is Christ the King,
   Whom shepherds guard and angels sing:
   Haste, haste to bring Him laud,
   The Babe, the Son of Mary!

2. So bring Him incense, gold and myrrh,
   Come peasant, King, to own Him,
   The King of kings salvation bring,
   Let loving hearts enthrone Him.
   Raise, raise the song on high,
   The virgin sings her lullaby:
   Joy, joy for Christ is born,
   The Babe, the Son of Mary

The First Nowell

1. The first Nowell the angel did say
   Was to certain poor shepherds, in fields as they lay,
   In fields where they lay keeping their sheep,
   On a cold winter's night that was so deep.
   Nowell, Nowell, Nowell, Nowell,
   Born is the King of Israel.

2. They looked up and saw a star,
   Shining in the east beyond them far,
   And to the earth it gave great light,
   And so it continued both day and night. *Nowell, ...*

3. And by the light of that same star,
   Three wise men came from country far;
   To seek for a king was their intent,
   And to follow the star where-ever it went. *Nowell ...*

4. Then entered in those wise men three,
   Most reverently upon their knee,
   And offered there, in his presence,
   Both gold and myrrh and frankincense. *Nowell, ...*

Angels We Have Heard on High

1. Angels we have heard on high
   Sweetly singing through the night,
   And the mountains in reply
   Echoing their brave delight.
   Gloria in excelsis Deo. Gloria in excelsis Deo.

2. Shepherds, why this jubilee?
   Why these songs of happy cheer?
   What great brightness did you see?
   What glad tidings did you hear?
   Gloria...

3. Come to Bethlehem and see
   Him whose birth the angels sing;
   Come, adore on bended knee,
   Christ, the Lord, the newborn King.
   Gloria...

Silent Night

1. Silent night, holy night,
   All is calm, all is bright
   Round yon virgin mother and child
   Holy infant so tender and mild,
   Sleep in heavenly peace,
   Sleep in heavenly peace.

2. Silent night, holy night,
   Shepherds quake at the sight,
   Glories stream from heaven afar,
   Heavenly hosts sing "Alleluia,
   Christ, the Savior is born!
   Christ, the Savior is born!"

3. Silent night, holy night,
   Son of God, love's pure light
   Radiant beams from thy holy face,
   With the dawn of redeeming grace,
   Jesus, Lord, at thy birth,
   Jesus, Lord, at thy birth.

Hanerot

What Child is This?

1. What Child is this, Who, laid to rest
   On Mary's lap is sleeping?
   Whom angels greet with anthems sweet,
   While shepherds watch are keeping?
   This, this is Christ the King,
   Whom shepherds guard and angels sing:
   Haste, haste to bring Him laud,
   The Babe, the Son of Mary!

2. So bring Him incense, gold and myrrh,
   Come peasant, King, to own Him,
   The King of kings salvation bring,
   Let loving hearts enthrone Him.
   Raise, raise the song on high,
   The virgin sings her lullaby:
   Joy, joy for Christ is born,
   The Babe, the Son of Mary

The First Nowell

1. The first Nowell the angel did say
   Was to certain poor shepherds, in fields as they lay,
   In fields where they lay keeping their sheep,
   On a cold winter's night that was so deep.
   Nowell, Nowell, Nowell, Nowell,
   Born is the King of Israel.

2. They looked up and saw a star,
   Shining in the east beyond them far,
   And to the earth it gave great light,
   And so it continued both day and night. *Nowell, ...*

3. And by the light of that same star,
   Three wise men came from country far;
   To seek for a king was their intent,
   And to follow the star where-ever it went. *Nowell ...*

4. Then entered in those wise men three,
   Most reverently upon their knee,
   And offered there, in his presence,
   Both gold and myrrh and frankincense. *Nowell, ...*

Angels We Have Heard on High

1. Angels we have heard on high
   Sweetly singing through the night,
   And the mountains in reply
   Echoing their brave delight.
   Gloria in excelsis Deo. Gloria in excelsis Deo.

2. Shepherds, why this jubilee?
   Why these songs of happy cheer?
   What great brightness did you see?
   What glad tidings did you hear?
   Gloria...

3. Come to Bethlehem and see
   Him whose birth the angels sing;
   Come, adore on bended knee,
   Christ, the Lord, the newborn King.
   Gloria...

Silent Night

1. Silent night, holy night,
   All is calm, all is bright
   Round yon virgin mother and child
   Holy infant so tender and mild,
   Sleep in heavenly peace,
   Sleep in heavenly peace.

2. Silent night, holy night,
   Shepherds quake at the sight,
   Glories stream from heaven afar,
   Heavenly hosts sing "Alleluia,
   Christ, the Savior is born!
   Christ, the Savior is born!"

3. Silent night, holy night,
   Son of God, love's pure light
   Radiant beams from thy holy face,
   With the dawn of redeeming grace,
   Jesus, Lord, at thy birth,
   Jesus, Lord, at thy birth.

Hanerot

What Child is This?

1. What Child is this, Who, laid to rest
   On Mary's lap is sleeping?
   Whom angels greet with anthems sweet,
   While shepherds watch are keeping?
   This, this is Christ the King,
   Whom shepherds guard and angels sing:
   Haste, haste to bring Him laud,
   The Babe, the Son of Mary!

2. So bring Him incense, gold and myrrh,
   Come peasant, King, to own Him,
   The King of kings salvation bring,
   Let loving hearts enthrone Him.
   Raise, raise the song on high,
   The virgin sings her lullaby:
   Joy, joy for Christ is born,
   The Babe, the Son of Mary

The First Nowell

1. The first Nowell the angel did say
   Was to certain poor shepherds, in fields as they lay,
   In fields where they lay keeping their sheep,
   On a cold winter's night that was so deep.
   Nowell, Nowell, Nowell, Nowell,
   Born is the King of Israel.

2. They looked up and saw a star,
   Shining in the east beyond them far,
   And to the earth it gave great light,
   And so it continued both day and night. *Nowell, ...*

3. And by the light of that same star,
   Three wise men came from country far;
   To seek for a king was their intent,
   And to follow the star where-ever it went. *Nowell ...*

4. Then entered in those wise men three,
   Most reverently upon their knee,
   And offered there, in his presence,
   Both gold and myrrh and frankincense. *Nowell, ...*

Angels We Have Heard on High

1. Angels we have heard on high
   Sweetly singing through the night,
   And the mountains in reply
   Echoing their brave delight.
   Gloria in excelsis Deo.   Gloria in excelsis Deo.

2. Shepherds, why this jubilee?
   Why these songs of happy cheer?
   What great brightness did you see?
   What glad tidings did you hear?
   Gloria...

3. Come to Bethlehem and see
   Him whose birth the angels sing;
   Come, adore on bended knee,
   Christ, the Lord, the newborn King.
   Gloria...

Silent Night

1. Silent night, holy night,
   All is calm, all is bright
   Round yon virgin mother and child
   Holy infant so tender and mild,
   Sleep in heavenly peace,
   Sleep in heavenly peace.

2. Silent night, holy night,
   Shepherds quake at the sight,
   Glories stream from heaven afar,
   Heavenly hosts sing "Alleluia,
   Christ, the Savior is born!
   Christ, the Savior is born!"

3. Silent night, holy night,
   Son of God, love's pure light
   Radiant beams from thy holy face,
   With the dawn of redeeming grace,
   Jesus, Lord, at thy birth,
   Jesus, Lord, at thy birth.

Hanerot

What Child is This?

1. What Child is this, Who, laid to rest
   On Mary's lap is sleeping?
   Whom angels greet with anthems sweet,
   While shepherds watch are keeping?
   This, this is Christ the King,
   Whom shepherds guard and angels sing:
   Haste, haste to bring Him laud,
   The Babe, the Son of Mary!

2. So bring Him incense, gold and myrrh,
   Come peasant, King, to own Him,
   The King of kings salvation bring,
   Let loving hearts enthrone Him.
   Raise, raise the song on high,
   The virgin sings her lullaby:
   Joy, joy for Christ is born,
   The Babe, the Son of Mary

The First Nowell

1. The first Nowell the angel did say
   Was to certain poor shepherds, in fields as they lay,
   In fields where they lay keeping their sheep,
   On a cold winter's night that was so deep.
   Nowell, Nowell, Nowell, Nowell,
   Born is the King of Israel.

2. They looked up and saw a star,
   Shining in the east beyond them far,
   And to the earth it gave great light,
   And so it continued both day and night. *Nowell, ...*

3. And by the light of that same star,
   Three wise men came from country far;
   To seek for a king was their intent,
   And to follow the star where-ever it went. *Nowell ...*

4. Then entered in those wise men three,
   Most reverently upon their knee,
   And offered there, in his presence,
   Both gold and myrrh and frankincense. *Nowell, ...*

Angels We Have Heard on High

1. Angels we have heard on high
   Sweetly singing through the night,
   And the mountains in reply
   Echoing their brave delight.
   Gloria in excelsis Deo. Gloria in excelsis Deo.

2. Shepherds, why this jubilee?
   Why these songs of happy cheer?
   What great brightness did you see?
   What glad tidings did you hear?
   Gloria...

3. Come to Bethlehem and see
   Him whose birth the angels sing;
   Come, adore on bended knee,
   Christ, the Lord, the newborn King.
   Gloria...

Silent Night

1. Silent night, holy night,
   All is calm, all is bright
   Round yon virgin mother and child
   Holy infant so tender and mild,
   Sleep in heavenly peace,
   Sleep in heavenly peace.

2. Silent night, holy night,
   Shepherds quake at the sight,
   Glories stream from heaven afar,
   Heavenly hosts sing "Alleluia,
   Christ, the Savior is born!
   Christ, the Savior is born!"

3. Silent night, holy night,
   Son of God, love's pure light
   Radiant beams from thy holy face,
   With the dawn of redeeming grace,
   Jesus, Lord, at thy birth,
   Jesus, Lord, at thy birth.

Hanerot

Nous Voici Dans La Ville
In The Town Of Bethlehem

French: Lucas le Moigne, c.1450
English: George W. Anthony, 1966

Anonymous, 15th Century

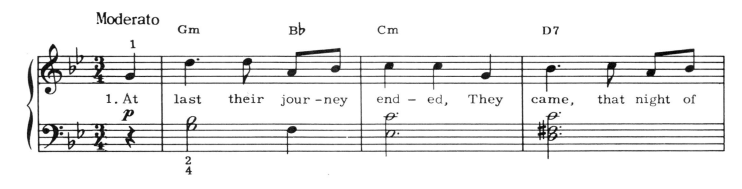

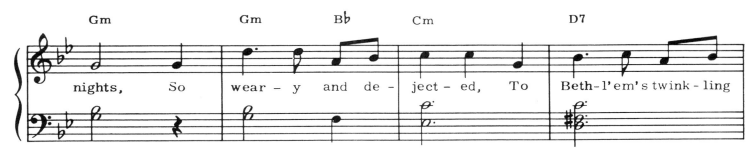

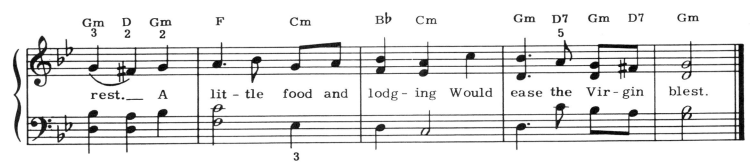

2. So then they asked the innkeep
   If he would give them room;
   "Oh no," said he, "I'm sorry,
   To tell you I have none."
   And Joseph was sore tried, but
   They wearily began
   Again to seek a room where
   His wife could have her son.

3. But then a woman told them
   A stable in the yard
   Was theirs if they did want it,
   She had no other space.
   Said Joseph, "Here we'll stay now,
   We have no other choice."
   And so they found a lodging
   In cold and lowly place.

414- 41072

CZECHOSLOVAKIA

Hajej, Nynej, Ježíšku

Little Jesus, Do Not Wake

Czech: Anonymous
English: Jeana Graham, 1963

Anonymous

2. Mary's little new-born Son, safe from harm,
Slumber now without alarm;
Little lamb of God come down, from above,
To all earth His gift of love.
While we rock you, rock you, rock you,
While we rock you, rock you, rock you;
Grant that we our whole lives through,
Find our joy in serving you.

414- 41072

GERMANY

Es Blühn Drei Rosen

There Are Three Roses

German: Anonymous
English: George W. Anthony, 1966

Anonymous

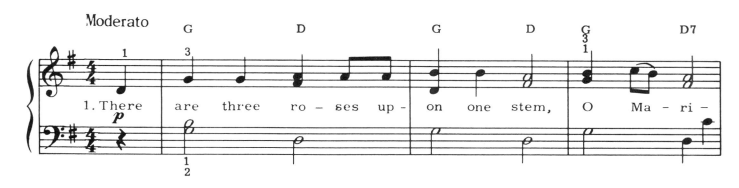

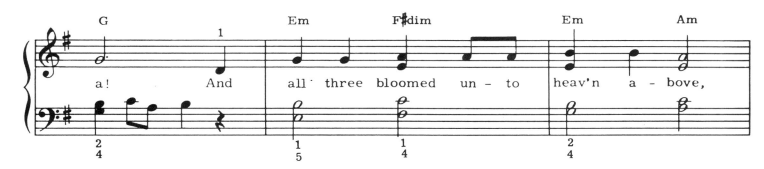

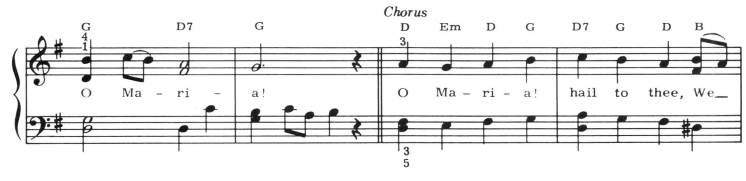

2. What lies so still in Maria's lap?
   O Maria!
   A little Baby so cold and bare,
   O Maria!
   Chorus

3. What do we see on Maria's head?
   O Maria!
   She wears a crown God has given her,
   O Maria!
   Chorus

414-41072

© Copyright 1966 by Theodore Presser Co.

PUERTO RICO

Pastores A Belén

To Bethlehem The Shepherds Go

Puerto Rican: Anonymous
English: Sybil Reid, 1966

Anonymous

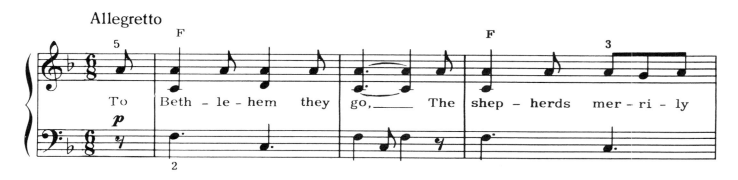

To Beth – le – hem they go,___ The shep – herds mer – ri – ly

trav – el To see the dear – est Babe,___ The Son of Jo – seph and

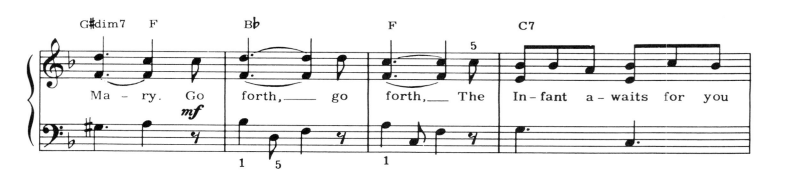

Ma – ry. Go forth,___ go forth,___ The In – fant a – waits for you

there,___ Go forth,___ go forth,___ The In – fant a – waits for you

414- 41072

UNITED STATES

March Of The Toys
(From "Babes In Toyland")

Ada Richter, 1966

Victor Herbert, 1903
(1859-1924)

414- 41072

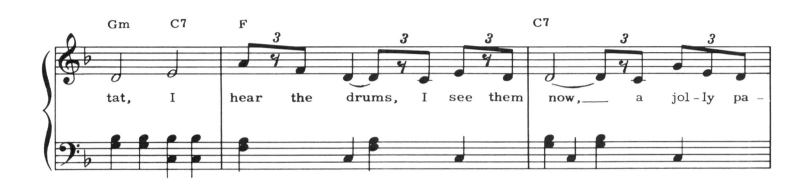

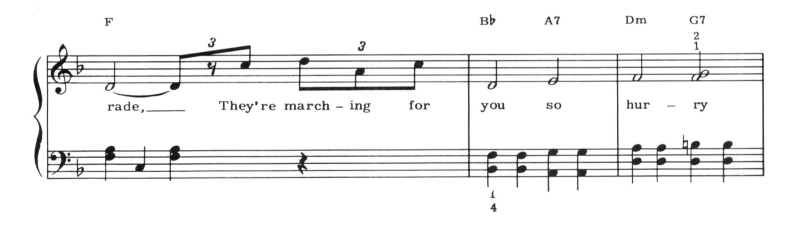

ITALY

Dormi, Dormi, O Bel Bambin

Sleep, O Sleep, My Lovely Child

Italian: Anonymous
English: Sybil Reid, 1966

Anonymous

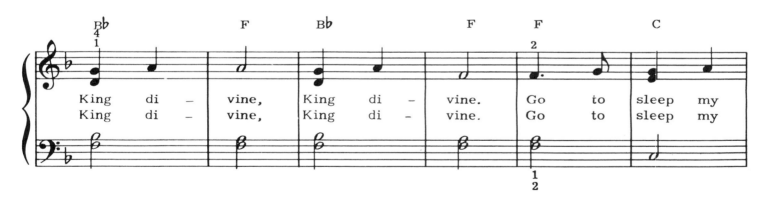

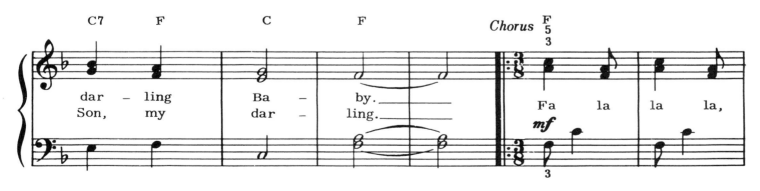

414-41072

SWEDEN

Nu Är Det Jul Igen

Now It Is Christmastime

Swedish: Anonymous
English: Roberta Carlson, 1966

Anonymous

414-41072

GERMANY

Morgen, Kinder, Wirds Was Geben

The Joy Of Christmas Day

German: Anonymous

English: George W. Anthony, 1966

Anonymous

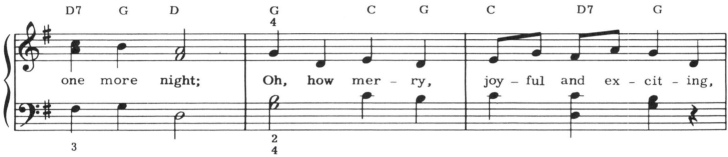

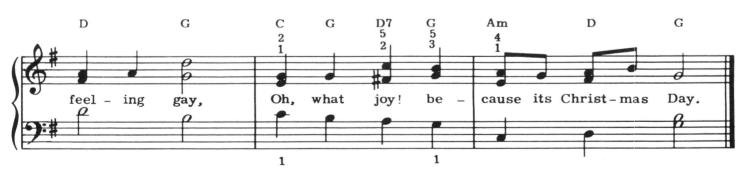

2. Think of all the many little candles
   All brightly shining on the tree;
   From the fireplace hang the little stockings
   Filled up with candy, you shall see.
   Can you still remember, Jay,
   How it was last Christmas Day?

3. It will be a lovely day for Christmas,
   Seems ev'ry year we have more fun;
   Mother, father, making preparations,
   They share the joy with everyone.
   You must learn to share this way
   On this joyful, happy Christmas Day.

414-41072

GERMANY

Zu Bethlehem Geboren
The Child In Bethlehem

German: Anonymous, 1638
English: George W. Anthony, 1966

Anonymous, 1638

2. The Child who comes this morn
   For all mankind was born.
   My heart, my hands, my pray'rs to Him
   I give, to be His own.
   Eia, Eia, My soul to be His own.

3. O dearest Child most holy,
   In joy I greet this day,
   That brings you to us all on earth,
   Who need you for their own.
   Eia, Eia, My soul to be His own.

414- 41072

SCOTLAND

Auld Lang Syne

1st verse, Anonymous
2nd verse, Robert Burns, c.1796
(1759-1796)

Anonymous, c.1792

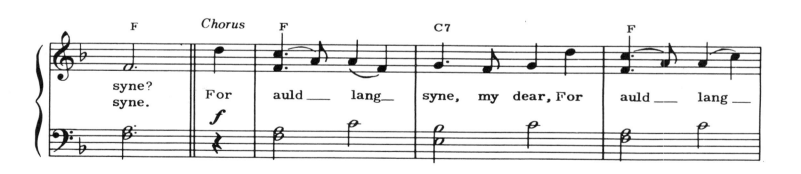

414- 41072